Radio, TV, and Sound System Diagnosis and Repair

Radio, TV, and Sound System Diagnosis and Repair

Walter Folger

Reston Publishing Company, Inc.
A Prentice-Hall Company
Reston, Virginia

Library of Congress Cataloging in Publication Data

Folger, Walter.
  Radio, TV, and sound system diagnosis and repair.

  Includes index.
  1. Radio—Repairing. 2. Television—Repairing.
3. Stereophonic sound systems—Repairing. 4. Public
address systems—Maintenance and repair. I. Title.
TK6553.F63   621.38′028   79-21995
ISBN 0-8359-6375-6

© 1980 by
Reston Publishing Company, Inc.
A Prentice-Hall Company
Reston, Virginia

10 9 8 7 6 5 4 3 2 1

Printed in the United States of America

Contents

Preface

With the rapid advance of electronic technology, particularly in the area of consumer electronics, the need has become apparent for a comprehensive state-of-the art text for trouble diagnosis and repair of radio, television, and sound systems. A generalized treatment of these topics makes this book appropriate both for self-instruction and for classroom use. Theory has been held to a minimum, and the troubleshooting aspects of modern electronic circuitry have been emphasized with equal stress on diagnostic procedures and repair techniques.

The general approach to these activities is outlined in the first chapter, with explanation of the three major steps that are involved. An introduction is provided for intermediate diagnostic steps, electrical and electronic quick checks, basic measurements, tool requirements, mechanical techniques, and comparison tests. In the second chapter, a survey of modern test equipment is provided. Analog and digital voltmeters, generators, oscilloscopes, acoustic level meters, video analyzers, and other basic units of test equipment are described and illustrated.

In the third chapter, the powerful diagnostic principles of mapping are developed, starting with elementary block diagrams and proceeding to DC flow diagrams, signal-flow diagrams, and functional diagrams. The author progresses into signal-path diagrams, picture and interconnection diagrams, elaborated diagrams, and skeleton schematic diagrams. Various combination mapping techniques are also exemplified. Next, the principles of malfunction analysis are covered in the fourth chapter. Possible and probable trouble areas are related to typical trouble symptoms. Evaluations of noise output, weak output, distorted output, intermittent operation, interference, audio rectification, failure-prone conditions, and phantom faults are provided.

The fifth chapter is concerned with hi-fi stereo system diagnosis and repair. Distortion checks, common technical errors, harmonic-distortion measurements, intermodulation-distortion measurements, frequency response checks, tone-burst tests, stereo separation measurements, audio quick tests, and other incidental topics are described and illustrated. In the sixth chapter, public-address trouble diagnosis and repair are covered. Typical systems are shown, with note of the popular 70.7 and 25 volt designs. PA acoustic environments are inspected and evaluated, and the principles of speech reinforcement are explained. Audio time delay basics, delay compensation, and delay reverberation are described, problems of positive feedback and equalization are examined, and practical audio signal-mixing methods are discussed. Planning and installation of both balanced and unbalanced lines are described and illustrated.

In the seventh chapter, radio receiver and transceiver trouble diagnosis and repair are considered in appropriate detail. Timely attention to CB troubleshooting, maintenance, and performance verification is included. The eighth chapter develops the principles of trouble diagnosis and repair techniques for solid-state black-and-white television receivers. Modern TV test-equipment applications are explained. This treatment is extended to solid-state color-TV receivers in the ninth chapter and is supplemented by set-up procedures and integrated-circuit notes in the tenth chapter. Modular design and modular repair are discussed in addition to older receiver arrangements.

It is assumed that the student has completed courses in basic electricity, electronics, and elementary radio theory. It is desirable that the student have had some previous exposure to television receiver principles and operation. The student should have completed a basic course in electronic instrumentation and measurements. However, an alert student can assimilate this text satisfactorily with the superficial knowledge of instruments gained from previous courses in physics and basic electricity and electronics. Mathematics has been held to a minimum, and graphical treatments of quantitative considerations have been utilized in the text. However, the student should have completed courses in arithmetic, algebra, geometry, and elementary trigonometry.

The author is indebted both to his associates and to numerous manufacturers, as credited throughout the text, for illustrative and technical data. No effort has been spared to make this text of maximum value to junior-college, vocational, and trade students, as well as to home-study and on-the-job personnel.

Chapter 1

General Approach

1-1 Three Major Steps

Three major steps are observed in most electronic system repair procedures:

1. Evaluation of trouble symptoms, with preliminary diagnosis of equipment malfunction.
2. Testing of logical conclusions.
3. Repair of defect and verification of normal operation.

The first step is most important. Unless this first step is carefully followed, an excessive amount of time and effort is likely to be wasted in futile random approaches. This first step involves careful observation of equipment response (if any) to input signals and equipment reaction to variation of operating and maintenance controls. In turn, this preliminary evaluation and diagnostic procedure will often lead the troubleshooter to probable or possible causes of malfunction. The second step comprises definitive tests of the various logical conclusions that have been established. These tests often include quick checks such as click tests and noise injection, as detailed subsequently. Modules may be substituted. Systematic signal-tracing or signal-substitution tests may be made. Eventually, all but one of the possible causes for malfunction will be eliminated—by specialized troubleshooting procedures, if necessary. Then, the third step is taken: repair of the defect(s) and final verification of system operation.

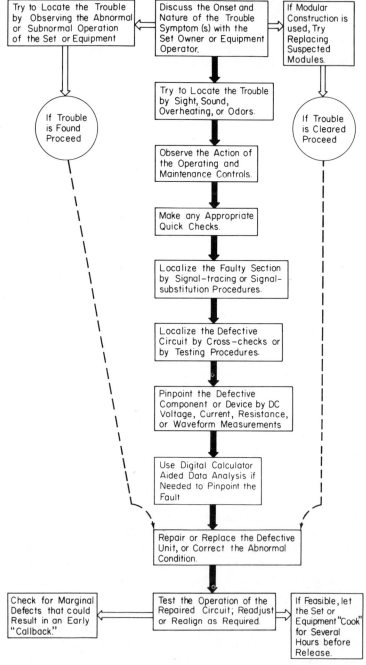

Fig. 1-1   Intermediate steps in electronic diagnostic and repair procedures.

1-2 Intermediate Steps

With reference to Figure 1-1, it is often helpful to discuss the onset and nature of the trouble symptom(s) with the set owner or equipment operator. Thereby, the troubleshooter can determine whether the malfunction developed gradually or suddenly, whether the present trouble symptoms were preceded by other kinds of symptoms, and whether the complaint may be a recurrent condition. Some of the simpler kinds of equipment faults can be quickly recognized from observation of subnormal operation. For instance, rasping and scratchy sound reproduction immediately points to a loose or warped voice coil in a speaker. As noted above, modular construction is utilized in some electronic equipment (Figure 1-2). In such a case, the troubleshooter's general approach may include replacement of suspected modules. Sometimes this quick-check procedure serves to immediately identify the trouble area and to return the equipment to normal operation. Note that a faulty module may be repaired or discarded, depending upon the failure— whether it is minor or catastrophic. Several companies specialize in module repair.*

When the cause of equipment malfunction is not immediately apparent, the experienced troubleshooter proceeds to seek the cause by sight (visual inspection), sound, overheating, or odors. If a thorough visual inspection is made, accompanied by cleaning and dusting if desirable, the cause of malfunction will often become apparent before the procedure is completed. However, if the troubleshooter must continue his search, it is advisable to operate the equipment and to listen for abnormal sounds, evidence of overheating, or various odors. As an illustration, an abnormal 60-Hz hum indicates a heavily overloaded power transformer. Snapping or crackling sounds point to high-voltage arcs. Odors of burned wax are caused by serious leakage in capacitors or badly overheated transformers. Burning resistors have a sharp pungent odor. Sometimes a circuit fault is not accompanied by symptoms that can be seen, heard, felt, or otherwise directly sensed. Accordingly, the cause of equipment malfunction must be determined by means of electrical and electronic tests and measurements.

With reference to Figure 1-3, two of the basic troubleshooting test procedures are termed signal-tracing and signal-substitution techniques. Thus, an oscilloscope may be used to signal-trace an AM radio receiver to determine the section where the signal is stopped, weakened, or distorted. Or an AM generator may be utilized to inject signals of suitable frequencies into the circuitry of an AM radio receiver to locate a stage that stops or weakens the test signal; the speaker is employed as an output indicator. Instead of an AM signal generator, preliminary signal-substitution tests may use a simple noise generator, as depicted in Figure 1-4. Although the output level and

* PTS Electronics, Inc., and Modular Electronics Services, Ltd.

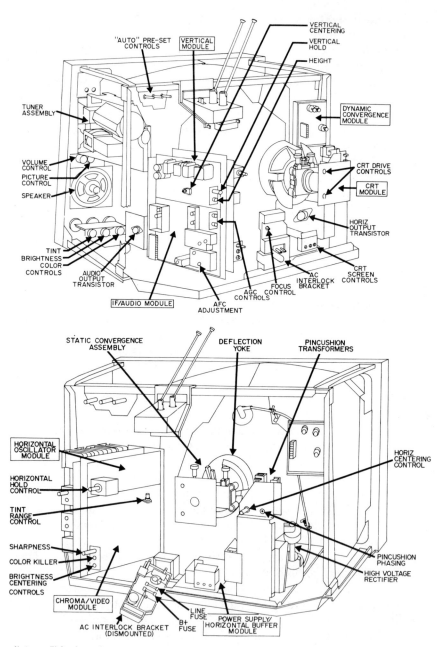

Note: This is only a representative layout, and is not a standard arrangement.

Fig. 1-2   Module identification in a typical color-TV receiver. (Courtesy, GE)

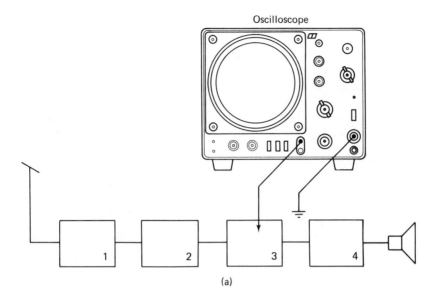

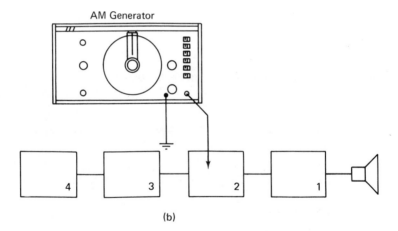

Fig. 1-3 **Signal tracing and signal substitution. (a) Signal tracing with the oscilloscope; (b) signal substitution with an AM signal generator.**

frequency cannot be controlled, a noise generator has the advantage of compactness; it is easy to use and can show whether a stage is workable or unworkable. Another type of quick-check, called a cross-check, is depicted

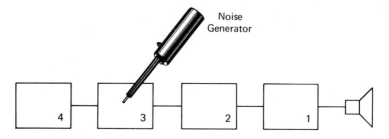

Fig. 1-4   A noise generator may be used in preliminary signal-substitution tests.

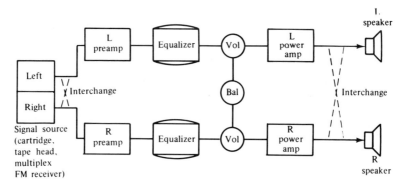

Fig. 1-5   Signal-source and speaker cross-checks.

in Figure 1-5. This kind of preliminary test is limited to stereo systems. It consists of temporarily interchanging the connections from the signal source to the L and R channels, and from the speakers to the L and R channels. A cross-check can be very helpful in preliminary trouble localization.

1-3   Quick-Checks

Another type of quick-check is shown in Figure 1-6; if it is suspected that a radio receiver is "dead" owing to failure of its local oscillator, the receiver under test may be placed near another operating receiver. In turn, the operating receiver is tuned to a broadcast station between 1 MHz and 1.5 MHz. Then the tuning dial of the "dead" receiver is varied from 545 kHz to 1.45 MHz. If a loud heterodyne squeal is produced by the "good" receiver at some point on the tuning dial, it is confirmed that the local oscillator is operating in the receiver under test. On the other hand, if a heterodyne squeal is not heard, it is indicated that the local oscillator is "dead" in the receiver under test. A related type of quick-check is pictured in Figure 1-7.

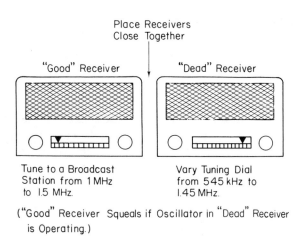

Place Receivers
Close Together

"Good" Receiver

"Dead" Receiver

Tune to a Broadcast
Station from 1 MHz
to 1.5 MHz.

Vary Tuning Dial
from 545 kHz to
1.45 MHz.

("Good" Receiver Squeals if Oscillator in "Dead" Receiver
is Operating.)

Fig. 1-6   Quick-check for suspected "dead" local oscillator.

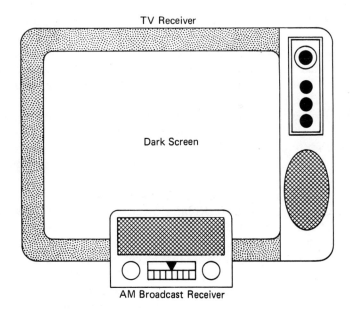

TV Receiver

Dark Screen

AM Broadcast Receiver

Operating horizontal-sweep
section generates harmonics
at 15,750-Hz intervals

Operating vertical-sweep
section generates harmonics
at 60-Hz intervals

**Fig. 1-7   Quick-check for suspected "dead" sweep section in a TV
receiver.**

Here, an AM broadcast receiver is used to determine whether the sweep section in a TV receiver may be "dead." Although the screen of the TV receiver is dark, harmonics from the sweep section will radiate into the radio receiver if the sweep section is operating. If the vertical-sweep section is operating, a 60-Hz hum will be heard from the speaker in the AM receiver; if the horizontal-sweep section is operating, a heterodyne squeal will be heard at 15.75-kHz intervals along the tuning dial of the AM broadcast receiver.

1-4   Electrical Measurements

In many situations, the defective component or device will not be apparent, although the faulty section in the equipment has been identified. In turn, the troubleshooter proceeds to pinpoint the malfunctioning component or device by means of DC voltage and resistance measurements, often supplemented by oscilloscope waveform analysis. Many component and device failures are accompanied by an abnormal DC voltage distribution in the associated circuitry. Similarly, abnormal point-to-point resistance values may occur. DC current measurements are sometimes informative, as detailed subsequently. Waveform checks will occasionally pinpoint a defective component that is not accompanied by any DC voltage, resistance, or current changes. Note in passing that a trouble symptom such as "weak output" or "distorted output" often results from a single fault, such as a defective transistor. However, this is not an invariable rule, and the troubleshooter must be on the alert for more than one fault that is responsible for a particular trouble symptom.

Evaluation and diagnosis of abnormal DC voltage distribution or abnormal resistance relations occasionally require various numerical calculations. These computations of circuit action with respect to measured values are facilitated by digital calculator aided data analysis. A comparatively elaborate hand-held digital calculator is depicted in Figure 1-8. A calculator can save considerable time and effort that would otherwise be spent with pencil-and-paper figuring. Note that electrical measurements are meaningful only to the extent that the troubleshooter understands their significance so that he can reason from a group of values to their logical conclusion. As an illustration, the DC voltages at the base, emitter, and collector of a transistor are interrelated; one type of defect will produce a particular pattern of abnormal DC voltage distribution, whereas another kind of defect will produce another kind of distribution pattern. All electrical values in electronic circuitry are based on Ohm's law, although their interrelations are not always obvious.

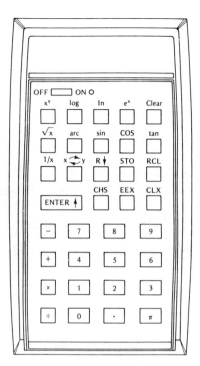

Fig. 1-8 A comparatively elaborate hand-held digital calculator.

1-5 Tools Used in Electronic System Repair

Various basic tools are required in radio, television, and sound system repair, as illustrated in Figure 1-9. Only simple hand tools are necessary in most repair jobs. Pliers, a diagonal cutter, standard screwdrivers, and wire strippers are often sufficient. Sometimes, Allen-head wrenches (Figure 1-10) are required. Note that both semiconductor devices and circuit boards are subject to damage unless good practices are observed and proper tools are employed. Semiconductors are quickly ruined by overheating. Accordingly, when soldering or unsoldering solid-state devices such as transistors, diodes, or integrated circuits, some form of heat-sink protection should be provided. In some situations, a pair of long-nose pliers will serve the purpose; the pliers are used to grasp the lead between the device and the point of soldering. However, when space is at a premium, a thin-profile heat sink must be used, as shown in Figure 1-11. If space permits, an ordinary alligator clip will serve as a heat sink.

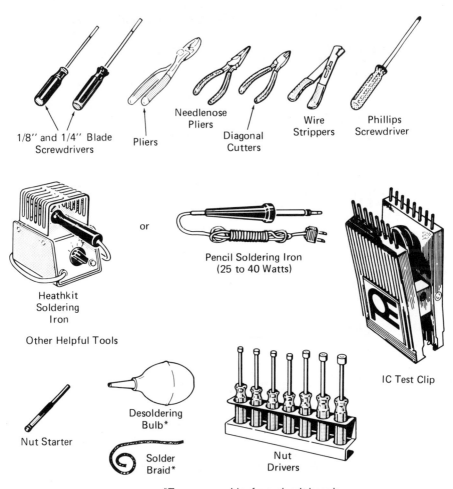

1/8" and 1/4" Blade Screwdrivers

Pliers

Needlenose Pliers

Diagonal Cutters

Wire Strippers

Phillips Screwdriver

Heathkit Soldering Iron

or

Pencil Soldering Iron (25 to 40 Watts)

IC Test Clip

Other Helpful Tools

Nut Starter

Desoldering Bulb*

Solder Braid*

Nut Drivers

*To remove solder from circuit boards.

Fig. 1-9   Basic tools used in radio, television, and sound system repair. (Courtesy, Heath Co.)

Fig. 1-10   A set of Allen-head wrenches.

(a)   (b)

Fig. 1-11   Heat sinks. (a) Conventional thin-profile heat sink; (b) alligator clip.

1-6 Mechanical Techniques

Printed-circuit (PC) boards can be mechanically damaged by excessive force or by the use of improper tools. PC boards can also be damaged by careless soldering procedure that permits excess solder to short-circuit adjacent conductors. Cold-solder joints can cause puzzling trouble symptoms such as intermittent operation. Good soldering technique is illustrated in Figure 1-12. PC-board operations require a small soldering iron or gun to avoid application of excessive heat and also to avoid mechanical interference with components and devices on the board. It is advisable to use a good quality solder of the 60/40 type—60 percent solder and 40 percent lead. Note too that semiconductor devices can be damaged by application of excessive leakage current from a soldering gun or iron. Electrical leakage between the heating element and the soldering tip can cause up to 117 volts to appear at the tip. The amount of leakage current depends on the value of the leakage resistance. It is good practice to provide the tip with a ground wire to a good ground connection, such as a cold water pipe.

Good soldering technique in connecting wires to terminal lugs is pictured in Figure 1-13. The basis of a reliable connection is ample mechanical attachment plus a proper solder bond. Specialized desoldering devices are very desirable for replacement of integrated circuits (IC), as shown in Figure 1-14. An IC desoldering tip enables the troubleshooter to desolder all of the IC terminals simultaneously. Note that excess solder that needs to be removed during a desoldering operation should be drawn up into a desoldering bulb. Specialized desoldering irons are available with attached bulbs for maximum convenience. Components on PC boards can be removed and replaced to best advantage as shown in Figure 1-15. Heat should be applied to the component lead, instead of the PC conductor. Bent-over ends of component leads can be straightened with a knife after the solder is melted. Then, the pigtail can be pulled through the PC board with a pair of pliers. Alternatively, leads can be snipped on the component side of the board with diagonal cutters, and the remaining ends of the leads then desoldered and withdrawn from the foil side of the board. The leads of the replacement component should be cleaned and formed and then threaded through the proper holes in the PC board until the component body rests against the

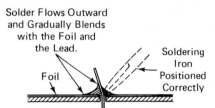

Solder Flows Outward
and Gradually Blends
with the Foil and
the Lead.

When you heat the lead and the circuit
board foil at the same time, the solder
will flow evenly onto the lead and the
foil. The solder will make a good
electrical connection between the lead
and the foil.

Poor Solder Connections

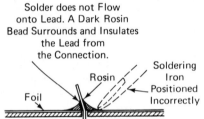

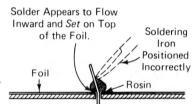

When the lead is not heated sufficiently,
the solder will not flow onto the lead
as shown above. To correct, reheat the
connection and, if necessary, apply a
small amount of additional solder to
obtain a good connection.

When the foil is not heated sufficiently
the solder will blob on the circuit
board as shown above. To correct,
reheat the connection and, if necessary,
apply a small amount of additional
solder to obtain a good connection.

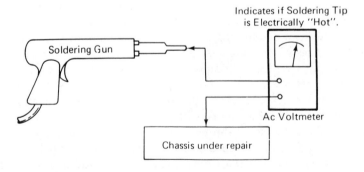

**Fig. 1-12   Good soldering technique, and electrical check method for
above-ground soldering iron. (Courtesy, Heath Co.)**

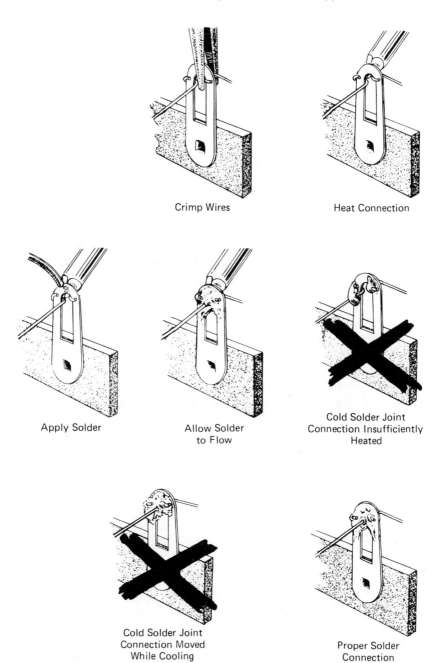

Crimp Wires

Heat Connection

Apply Solder

Allow Solder
to Flow

Cold Solder Joint
Connection Insufficiently
Heated

Cold Solder Joint
Connection Moved
While Cooling

Proper Solder
Connection

Fig. 1-13   Solder connections to terminal lugs. (Courtesy, Heath Co.)

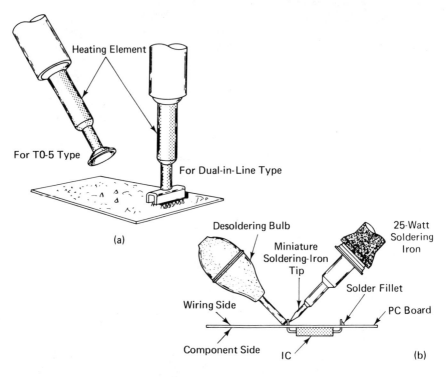

Fig. 1-14   Desoldering technique for integrated circuits. (a) Specialized desoldering tips; (b) desoldering bulb removes excess solder.

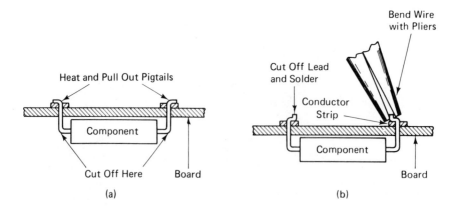

Fig. 1-15   How a printed-circuit component is replaced. (a) Removing the defective component; (b) installing a replacement component.

surface of the board. Leads should then be clipped and bent on the foil side of the board as shown in Figure 1-15. The pigtails may then be soldered to the PC conductors.

1-7 Comparison Tests

Diagnostic procedures are occasionally hampered owing to lack of a repair manual or service data for a particular unit of electronic equipment. In such a case, the technician is thrown completely upon his own resources. If a similar unit that is in good working condition is available, or can be inspected, considerable useful data can be obtained by means of comparison tests. For instance, normal DC operating voltages, resistance values, and waveforms can be determined. Note also that it is not essential to make comparison tests on identical models in many cases. That is, different models of a particular television receiver, for example, may have sufficiently similar design features that considerable useful data are obtainable. Expertise in "tough-dog" situations of this sort can be acquired only by a combination of study and experience.

Review Questions

1. What is the first major step to be observed in most electronic repair procedures?
2. Name two intermediate steps in electronic diagnosis procedures.
3. Why does rasping and scratchy sound reproduction throw suspicion upon the speaker?
4. How many modules are utilized in a typical color TV receiver?
5. Distinguish between signal-tracing and signal-substitution tests.
6. Describe a typical quick-check for a "dead" radio receiver.
7. Are single faults or multiple faults most frequently encountered?
8. Explain several of the basic tools used in radio, TV, and sound-system repair.
9. What are the essentials of good soldering technique?
10. When are comparison tests valuable in diagnostic procedures?

Survey of Modern Test Equipment

2-1 General Requirements

More types and varieties of test and measuring equipment are now used in radio, television, and sound system diagnosis and repair than in the past (see Figure 2-1). However, the most basic requirements have not changed. Thus, some form of volt-ohm-milliammeter (VOM or multimeter) is indispensable. Most instruments in this category measure DC voltage, resistance, AC voltage, and DC current values. One of the chief considerations in selection of a VOM is its input resistance (sensitivity). Sensitivities range from 1000 ohms/volt to 100,000 ohms/volt. A high value of input resistance is desirable to minimize circuit loading in high-resistance (high-impedance) configurations and thereby maximize indication accuracy. Transistor multimeters (TVOM's or FET meters), such as illustrated in Figure 2-2, are generally preferred because of their high input resistance (15 megohms on DC voltage ranges) and also for their hi-pwr and lo-pwr ohmmeter functions that facilitate measurements in solid-state circuitry.

With reference to Figure 2-3, many repairmen prefer digital multimeters to analog multimeters. A digital voltmeter (DVM) is highly accurate; for instance, the illustrated instrument is rated for 0.5 percent accuracy on DC voltage indication. It has 15-megohm input resistance for minimization of circuit disturbance in high-resistance configurations. The test probe contains a 200-kΩ isolation resistor; this feature minimizes capacitive loading in high-frequency circuitry. It also provides hi-pwr and lo-pwr ohms functions; the low-level test voltage (0.08 volt) employed on the lo-pwr ohms

Audio Frequencies: 20 Hz to 20 kHz	Video Frequencies: 0 to 4 MHz	Intermediate Frequencies: 455 kHz to 47.25 MHz	Broadcast Radio Frequencies: 550 kHz to 108 MHz
Audio Oscillator	Video-sweep Generator	AM Signal Generator	AM Signal Generator
Audio Sweep Generator	Test-pattern Generator	IF Sweep Generator	FM Signal Generator
Oscilloscope	Square-wave Generator	Test-pattern Generator	Signal Tracer
Harmonic Distortion Meter	Oscilloscope	Oscilloscope	Oscilloscope
Intermodulation Analyzer	Semiconductor Tester	Signal Tracer	Semiconductor tester
Square-wave Generator	Transistor Multimeter	Semiconductor Tester	Transistor Multimeter
Tone-burst Generator	Capacitor Checker	Transistor Multimeter	Capacitor Checker
Impedance Bridge	Color-bar Generator	Capacitor Checker	Stereo FM Multiplex Generator
Semiconductor Tester	Bar Sweep (Multi-burst) Generator	Stereo FM multiplex Generator	Frequency Counter
Transistor Multimeter			
Capacitor Checker			
Sound Level Meter			
Noise Generator			

Broadcast Television Frequencies: 54 to 890 MHz	Two-way Radio Frequencies: 37.02 to 465.5 MHz	Digital Equipment Frequencies: Up to 50 MHz
VHF and UHF Sweep and Marker Generators	Lab-type AM and FM Signal Generators	Logic Probe
Test Pattern Generator	Deviation Meter	Logic Pulser
Oscilloscope	RF Wattmeter	Logic Clip
Semiconductor Tester	Digital Frequency Counter	Logic Comparator
Transistor Multimeter	Transistor Multimeter	Current Tracer
Capacitor Checker	Tube Tester	Oscilloscope
Kilovoltmeter	Transistor Tester	Data Domain Analyzer
Field Strength Meter	SWR Meter	
	CB Analyzer	

Fig. 2-1   Test instruments used in various areas of electronic troubleshooting.

Fig. 2-2   A modern field-effect multimeter. (Courtesy, Sencore)

Fig. 2-3   A high-performance digital multimeter. (Courtesy, Sencore)

function avoids "firing" of semiconductor junctions and integrated circuits (ICs), and thereby multiplies the number of in-circuit resistance measurements that can be made in solid-state circuitry. Auto-polarity operation is provided; a "+" or a "−" indication is displayed, depending upon the polarity of the voltage under test. The instrument measures up to 2000 DC volts, 1000 AC volts, 20 megohms, and 2 amperes. Its voltage resolution is 1 millivolt (mV). The DVM is powered by self-contained batteries.

2-2   Signal Generators

Generators rank next in basic importance; many specialized types are available. However, a versatile AF/AM/FM generator such as pictured in Figure 2-4 has a wide range of application and need be supplemented only by a TV generator. The instrument shown in Figure 2-4 provides 400-Hz audio sine-wave and square-wave signal outputs, 525- to 1625-kHz AM output, 262- and 455-kHz IF (intermediate-frequency) output, 87- to 109-MHz FM coverage, 10.7-MHz IF output and FM IF sweep output, with stereo-FM multiplex test signals including 19-kHz and 38-kHz subcarrier signals. A 67-kHz trap signal is also provided. Next, a television sweep gen-

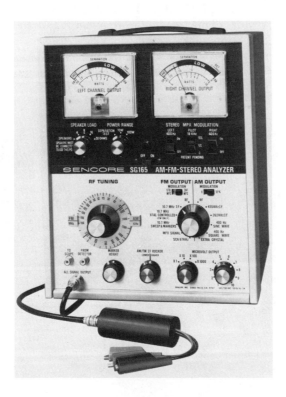

Fig. 2-4   A versatile audio and radio frequency signal generator. (Courtesy, Sencore)

erator is illustrated in Figure 2-5. It supplies a VHF sweep signal, 43-MHz IF sweep signal, 3.58-MHz chroma sweep signal, and crystal-controlled marker outputs. A post-injection marker system is provided to avoid the possibility of overload distortion.

Shops that specialize in audio service regard a low-distortion audio generator as essential; a few technicians also use audio sweep generators. A shop that specializes in radio servicing employs a standard AM signal generator; if CB, scanner-monitor, and two-way radios are also serviced, the technicians require a laboratory type AM/FM signal generator. The chief distinction between service-type and lab-type signal generators is the high accuracy provided by the latter over its entire frequency range. Most lab-type signal generators also have calibrated output facilities, whereby the operator can measure the number of microvolts that are applied to the radio under test. A specialized lab-type signal generator designed for citizens band (CB) service is illustrated in Figure 2-6. This instrument provides carrier, upper-sideband (USB) and lower-sideband (LSB) output on all 40 CB channels, with intermediate-frequency (IF) outputs from 375 kHz to 12 MHz. Audio outputs are provided at 400 Hz and 1 kHz. A built-in frequency counter provides digital readout of frequency, and the output attenuator is calibrated in microvolts.

Shops that engage in color-TV service require a specialized color signal generator for convergence procedures. With reference to Figure 2-7, a stan-

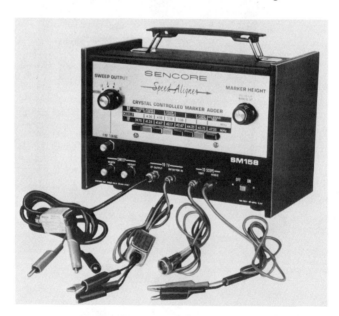

Fig. 2-5 A high-quality television sweep and marker generator. (Courtesy, Sencore)

Fig. 2-6   A specialized lab-type CB signal generator. (Courtesy, Sencore)

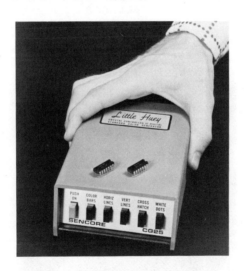

Fig. 2-7   A standard color signal generator. (Courtesy, Sencore)

dard color generator provides a color-bar (keyed-rainbow) pattern, horizontal-line and vertical-line patterns, a crosshatch pattern, and a white-dot pattern. The color-bar pattern comprises 10 vertical bars ranging through reds and blues to green. Fourteen lines are provided in the horizontal-line pattern, and 10 lines are provided in the vertical-line pattern. The crosshatch pattern consists of a superposition of the horizontal and vertical line patterns. The white-dot pattern consists of 140 dots, which are adjustable in size to meet the personal preference of the operator. RF (Radio Frequency) output is available on very-high-frequency (VHF) channels 2 through 6. The instrument is powered by self-contained batteries.

2-3 Oscilloscopes

Most electronic technicians consider the oscilloscope to be the third ranking instrument in the basic group. An oscilloscope is fundamentally a voltmeter, although it is a comparatively sophisticated type of instrument that displays the variation of an AC voltage in time; it also shows instantaneous waveform values. An oscilloscope indicates frequency values and can also be used for phase measurements. Modern oscilloscopes are designed to measure time intervals between any two chosen points along a waveform. An oscilloscope widely used in TV service is illustrated in Figure 2-8. This is a basic single-trace instrument with calibrated vertical attenuator and triggered time base. It has a vertical-amplifier bandwidth of 8 MHz, with a sensitivity of 10 mV/cm. The time-base range is from 0.2 microseconds per

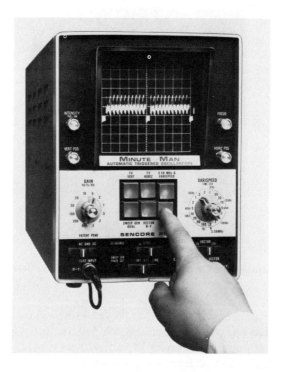

Fig. 2-8   A high-quality service-type oscilloscope. (Courtesy, Sencore)

centimeter (μsec/cm) to 0.1 sec/cm. It also provides preset TV vertical and horizontal deflection rates, plus a 3.58-MHz preset deflection rate. A 5-times sweep-expansion function is included, with a 60-Hz line-sweep facility for sweep-alignment applications. The instrument is also designed for vector-scope application. It may be used with a low-capacitance probe to minimize circuit loading, or with a demodulator probe for high-frequency signal-tracing tests.

A comparatively sophisticated type of TV service oscilloscope is pictured in Figure 2-9. This is a dual-trace instrument with phase-locked vertical channels to facilitate comparison tests of waveforms. It has a vertical-amplifier response to 8 MHz with a sensitivity rating of 5 mV/cm. A triggered time base is provided with a range from 0.1 μsec per cm to 0.1 sec per cm. The time base may be switched to free-running mode, if desired, with a repetition rate from 1 Hz to 1 MHz. Both vertical channels have input attenuators calibrated in peak-to-peak (P-P) volts per centimeter. The waveforms in the vertical channels may be displayed in either the alternate or the chopped mode. The instrument is also designed for vectorscope application in low-level circuits; the chroma waveforms are stepped up through the scope amplifiers. A low-capacitance probe or probes may be utilized to minimize circuit loading. A demodulator probe may also be used for signal-tracing tests in high-frequency circuitry, or in video-frequency response checks.

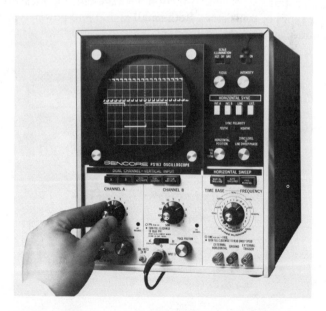

Fig. 2-9   **A comparatively sophisticated TV service oscilloscope. (Courtesy, Sencore)**

2-4 Secondary Test and Measuring Equipment

Some types of secondary test and measuring equipment are regarded as essential by various electronic troubleshooters. Thus, many electronic repairmen consider a semiconductor tester to be in the basic instrument category. A comprehensive tester that accommodates both biploar and unipolar transistors is illustrated in Figure 2-10. This is an out-of-circuit instrument; the transistor under test must be disconnected from its circuit. A bipolar transistor is checked for leakage current and for beta value; a unipolar transistor is checked for leakage current and for transconductance. Transconductance values are indicated in micromho units. Both small-signal and power-type transistors are accommodated by this type of instrument. It is powered by self-contained batteries.

Consider next the automatic transistor-FET analyzer illustrated in Figure 2-11. This is a combined in-circuit and out-of-circuit tester. The in-circuit test is based on the ability of a transistor to amplify, although a measurement of the amplification factor cannot be made with precision because of indeterminate shunt circuit impedances. Hence, the in-circuit indication is provided on an uncalibrated Good-Bad scale. Supplementary indication is provided by a "beep" tone in the event that the instrument indication is in the Good sector of the scale. Out-of-circuit tests include beta measurements for bipolar transistors and transconductance measurements for unipolar transistors, and junction leakage-current measurements for both basic types of transistors. Both small-signal and power-type transistors are accommodated by the instrument.

Fig. 2-10   A comprehensive transistor tester. (Courtesy, B&K Precision, Division of Dynascan Corp.)

Fig. 2-11 A transistor tester that includes in-circuit checking facilities. (Courtesy, Sencore)

2-5 Sound Level Meter

Among the various classes of secondary test and measuring instruments, audio technicians generally regard the sound-level meter (Figure 2-12) as comparatively important. It is used primarily to check the characteristics of acoustic environments. The instrument comprises a high-fidelity condenser microphone, a battery-powered integrated-circuit amplifier, and a meter calibrated in decibels. Six sound-level ranges are provided, with coverage from 60 dB to 126 dB, referenced to the standard acoustic zero-dB level of 0.002 microbar (μbar). Both A and C weightings are provided for indication modes. The A weighting provides virtually uniform response over the frequency range from 32 Hz to 8 kHz. This mode of indication provides measurement of the physical level of sound energy in the listening area at the frequency or frequencies of test. On the other hand, the C weighting provides a bass-attenuation response that follows the hearing characteristic of the human ear. This mode of indication is proportional to phon units, and measures loudness units instead of decibel units.

This type of sound-level meter provides a choice of fast or slow meter

Fig. 2-12   A sound level meter is used to check acoustic environments. (Courtesy, Radio Shack)

response; fast response indicates peak values of transient sound waves whereas slow response indicates average values of sound waveforms. It is often advantageous to mount a sound-level meter on a tripod so that noise from the operator's hand and sound reflections from his body do not impair the indication accuracy. Tripod mounting is also a convenience when a sound-level meter is used with auxiliary equipment, such as an oscilloscope. Note that if the operator stands between the meter and a sound source, an indication error of several dB can be anticipated in the frequency range above 100 Hz. It is good practice to position a sound-level meter so that the principal sound wavefront arrives at right angles to the face of the condenser microphone. However, the microphone is essentially omnidirectional so that small error is incurred in the event that the sound wavefront arrives at an arbitrary angle.

2-6   Video Analyzer

Television technicians generally regard a video analyzer as a comparatively important test instrument in the secondary class. This is a generator type of tester. It provides white-dot and crosshatch patterns for convergence tests and adjustments, and a gated-rainbow color-bar pattern for troubleshooting chroma circuitry. Modulated UHF, VHF, and IF test signals are available. The video analyzer also supplies two bar-sweep (multiburst) patterns. One pattern comprises ten vertical bars with frequencies of 188 kHz,

755 kHz, 1.51 MHz, 3.02 MHz, 3.08 MHz, 3.56 MHz, and 4.08 MHz, plus three black, gray, and white shading bars. The other pattern consists of three vertical bars with frequencies of 3.08 MHz, 3.56 MHz, and 4.08 MHz, phase-locked to the master oscillator in the generator. A modulated 4.5-MHz FM sound carrier is also provided. The output level is adjustable over a range from 100 to 5000 μV. A peak-to-peak voltmeter is included with ranges up to 1000 V. This meter is also provided with center-scale reference for peak and null adjustments. The video analyzer also has a built-in ringing-test facility to check flyback transformers and yokes. Sync, sweep-drive, and keying pulses are also available for checking sync, deflection, and AGC (automatic gain control) circuitry.

The exemplified video analyzer provides modulated IF output at a frequency of 45.75 MHz for use in tuner-substitution and signal-substitution tests. Trap-adjustment signals are available at 39.75 MHz, 41.25 MHz, and 47.25 MHz, with 1-kHz amplitude modulation. The intercarrier-sound test signal has a deviation of ± 15 kHz. Ringing tests are indicated on a go/no-go type of scale; these are in the quick-check category. A video tape recording (VTR) test signal is also provided. VTR chroma-processing stages are checked with the color-bar and chroma-bar signals, and luminescent stages are checked with the bar-sweep signal. VTR servo circuits are tested with composite sync signals. The video analyzer includes a built-in power supply for powering modules or other receiver subsections in bench-servicing operations. Another type of video analyzer in extensive use has similar signal-substitution and testing functions, except that it provides a standard test pattern for picture analysis, instead of a bar-sweep signal.

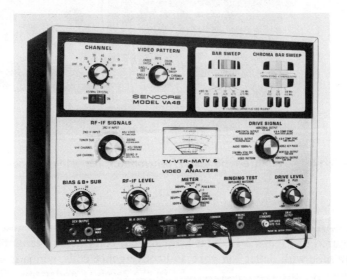

Fig. 2-13   **Appearance of a video analyzer. (Courtesy, Sencore)**

2-7 Picture-Tube Testers

A picture-tube tester/rejuvenator as exemplified in Figure 2-14 is another widely used secondary test instrument. It provides emission, tracking, and leakage (shorts) checks, with a series of cathode rejuvenation voltages. Emission values are indicated on a go/no-go type of scale. High-voltage scales for 10-kV focus potential and 50-kV accelerating potential permit the technician to distinguish between picture-tube defects and supply-voltage faults. Heater supply voltages up to 14 V are available, with grid-cathode bias voltages from 20 V to 70 V. The tracking test is made on the basis of comparative emission currents of the three electron guns in the color picture tube. Five cathode rejuvenation voltages are provided; the first two levels are comparatively low and are automatically timed. If restoration at these two levels is unsatisfactory, a higher current level automatically cycled three times may be utilized. In the case of a very weak picture tube, the technician may make a final attempt at rejuvenation with the two manual (untimed) control settings.

Fig. 2-14   Picture-tube tester/rejuvenator. (Courtesy, Sencore)

An extensively used companion device is a picture-tube test jig, such as pictured in Figure 2-15. This arrangement comprises a standard color picture tube with deflection yoke and convergence coils, which is used to substitute for the color picture tube in the receiver under test. Thereby, the technician can quickly distinguish between circuit malfunction and picture-tube faults in the receiver. A kilovoltmeter is built into the test jig for monitoring the high-voltage output from the receiver. Test connections from the test jig to the receiver are made with extension cables. Although the picture tube in the test jig may be overscanned or underscanned in various situations, depending upon the degree of match that the test assembly provides to the receiver assembly, it provides the troubleshooter with highly informative test data.

Fig. 2-15   A picture-tube test jig. (Courtesy, TeleMatic)

2-8   Miscellaneous Test and Measuring Equipment

There is no sharp dividing line between essential, secondary, and miscellaneous test equipment. An electronic repairman in a high-fidelity shop is likely to regard a harmonic distortion meter and an intermodulation analyzer as secondary test instruments, whereas a technician in a CB or two-way radio shop is likely to consider these instruments as miscellaneous or useless types. In other words, a professional hi-fi serviceman places great emphasis on low-distortion operation, whereas communication systems generally operate with considerable distortion—the only criterion is intelligibility. A CB or two-way radio repairman usually regards a frequency counter such as illustrated in Figure 2-16 as a secondary or possibly essential instrument, whereas a television technician generally considers it to be a miscellaneous or even useless instrument.

A tuner substitution unit (Figure 2-17) is used by many television servicemen to quick-check suspected tuners in black-and-white and color receivers. This instrument consists of a VHF-UHF tuner with a low-

Fig. 2-16   A versatile frequency counter. (Courtesy, Sencore)

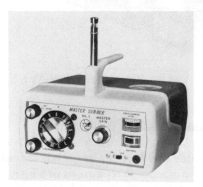

Fig. 2-17   A portable VHF tuner substitution unit. (Courtesy, Castle Electronics)

impedance IF output for injection into the receiver's IF strip. It includes a built-in carrier-level meter so that the operator can determine whether the incoming signal is being applied at normal level to the receiver under test. A whip-type antenna is provided for operation in strong-signal areas; an outdoor antenna can be connected to the instrument for operation in weak-signal areas. The unit is powered by self-contained batteries. In far-fringe areas, a tuner substitution unit with internally generated crosshatch and white-dot patterns may be preferred, as exemplified in Figure 2-18. It provides a low-impedance IF output for injection into the receiver's IF strip.

Fig. 2-18   A tuner substitution unit that provides crosshatch and white-dot patterns. (Courtesy, TeleMatic)

Fig. 2-19   A DC kilovoltmeter used in TV troubleshooting procedures. (Courtesy, TeleMatic)

Some type of kilovoltmeter is considered as an important type of miscellaneous test equipment by color-TV technicians, although many repairmen "get by" in black-and-white troubleshooting without means for high-voltage measurement. A VOM or TVOM is often used with a high-voltage probe; the multiplier resistor in the probe must be selected to match the input resistance of the particular voltmeter. In turn, the probe will multiply the scale indication by 100 or 1000, for example. A direct-reading kilovoltmeter (Figure 2-19) may be used with a high-voltage probe, or the meter may be attached to or built into the handle of the probe (Figure 2-20). As seen in Figures 2-14 and 2-15, high-voltage measuring facilities are built into certain types of test equipment for operating convenience. When the output from the high-voltage section is subnormal, the flyback transformer or yoke often comes under suspicion. In turn, technicians frequently check these components with a yoke and flyback tester such as shown in Figure 2-21. This instrument provides a transient ringing test on a go/no-go basis. A kilovolt scale is included so that high-voltage values can be measured with the use of an auxiliary high-voltage probe.

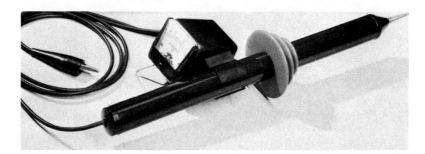

Fig. 2-20 A high-voltage DC probe designed for use with a clip-on volt-meter. (Courtesy, Radio Shack)

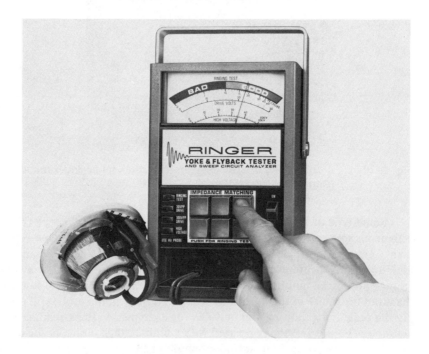

Fig. 2-21 A yoke and flyback tester. (Courtesy, Sencore)

2-9   Bench Power Supply

A regulated bench power supply such as illustrated in Figure 2-22 is often an important unit of miscellaneous equipment. It is useful to power modules that are being repaired, to substitute for defective power supplies in amplifiers and receivers, to monitor the current demand of equipment under test, and to recharge batteries such as alkaline cells. A component and device substitution box, as exemplified in Figure 2-23, is a welcome time-saver in various diagnostic and repair operations. In the event that a replacement resistor, capacitor, or rectifier is not immediately available, a quick-check can be made with the substitution box to determine whether normal operation is resumed when a known good component or device is patched into the circuit. In other situations, service data may not be available, so that the correct value for a replacement is not known. In such a case, a burned-out resistor can be patched from the substitution box, and its value varied to determine the requirement for optimum operation.

Fig. 2-22   **A regulated bench power supply. (Courtesy, Sencore)**

Fig. 2-23 A resistor, capacitor, and rectifier substitution box. (Courtesy, Sencore)

Review Questions

1. What is the indispensable test instrument for diagnosis of radio, TV, and sound-system malfunctions?

2. Why do many repairmen prefer DVM's over VOM's?

3. Name the basic generator used in a radio repair shop, a stereo service shop, a TV repair shop.

4. Explain the basic advantage that an oscilloscope provides over a TVM.

5. How does an in-circuit transistor tester differ from an out-of-circuit transistor tester?

6. Where does a sound-level meter find its principal field of application?

7. Describe the chief features of a video analyzer.

8. Distinguish between a picture-tube tester and a picture-tube test jig.

9. Why is a frequency counter a virtually essential instrument for a CB repair shop?

10. How does a high-voltage DC probe function?

Chapter 3
Mapping Techniques

3-1　General Principles

Most electronic troubleshooting and diagnosis procedures are guided by various mapping techniques. Block diagrams, schematic diagrams, signal-path and signal-flow charts, functional diagrams, equivalent circuits, layout diagrams, and related mapping techniques are often essential during preliminary diagnostic procedures. Four basic types of diagrams are exemplified in Figure 3-1. A simple block diagram, as depicted in (a) indicates the chief electronic sections in the equipment with their basic signal-channel relations. A direct-current flow diagram as shown in (b) combines a simple block diagram with current paths and values. As detailed subsequently, a DC flow diagram can be very informative in preliminary diagnostic procedures. Next, a signal-flow diagram is pictured in (c); three separate but related signals enter the composite signal amplifier and branch out into individual signal sections. A functional diagram, depicted in (d), is essentially a representation of the relations among the amplifying, signal-generating, and nonlinear signal-processing functions in an electronic unit. Note that a cross enclosed in a circle denotes any nonlinear function, such as a heterodyne mixer, a detector, a modulator, a switching bridge, or a rectifier-doubler.

An example of a schematic diagram (with corresponding functional diagram) is seen in Figure 3-2. A schematic diagram is extensively detailed in comparison with a block diagram. The schematic diagram is usually consulted after preliminary analysis of a trouble symptom with respect to a

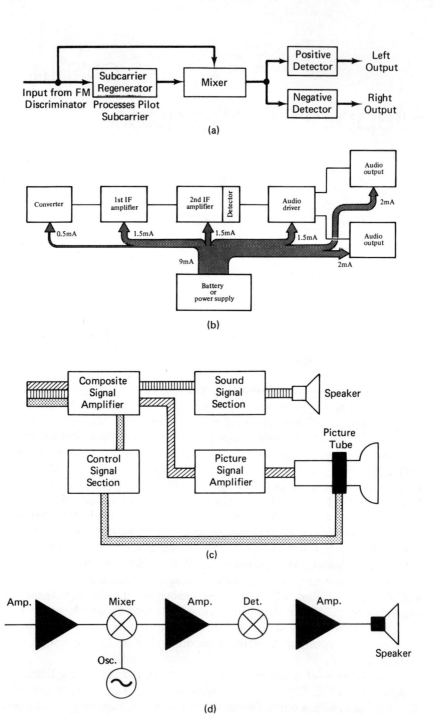

Fig. 3-1 **Basic types of diagrams used in mapping techniques. (a) Elementary block diagram; (b) DC flow diagram; (c) signal-flow diagram; (d) functional diagram.**

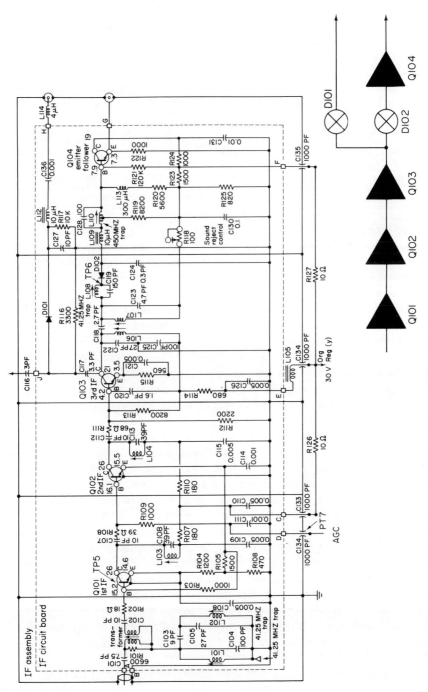

Fig. 3-2   Schematic diagram of an IF printed-circuit board.

block diagram. Note that this schematic diagram indicates resistance and capacitance values, trap frequencies, normal DC operating voltages at transistor terminals, supply-voltage value, control functions, and PC board terminals. Next, consider the layout diagram shown in Figure 3-3; this layout diagram corresponds to the schematic diagram in Figure 3-2. A layout diagram is a form of picture diagram that is of great assistance in routine troubleshooting procedures. Each resistor, capacitor, inductor, diode, and transistor is identified, both from the foil side and from the component side of the PC board. Thus, the troubleshooter can quickly turn his attention from the schematic diagram to the layout diagram and locate any particular component or device without difficulty.

3-2 Signal-Path Diagrams

Signal-path diagrams are a generalized type of signal-flow diagrams. With reference to Figure 3-4(a), the signal that is being processed may flow through several functional sections that operate in series—this is termed a linear signal path. Note that a linear signal path may proceed through linear circuitry, through nonlinear circuitry, or both. An example of a linear signal path is an audio preamplifier. Next, as shown in (b), the signal that is being processed may follow a divergent path. An example of a divergent signal path is the circuit action in a stereo decoder. Conversely, the signal that is being processed may follow a convergent signal path as shown in (c); an example is the circuit action in an audio mixer. Again, as depicted in (d), two signal sources may converge into a single section and emerge after processing as the divergent signals. An example of a convergent-divergent signal path is the circuit action of an audio mixer followed by a crossover network.

Another basic type of signal path involves a feedback loop, as exemplified in Figure 3-5(a). An example of this configuration is an audio preamplifier with negative feedback. Still another basic form of signal path employs a switching facility, as depicted in (b). A switching signal path is used, for example, in the sampling network of a dual-trace oscilloscope. Generalized signal-path diagrams may be modified to include functional sections, as shown in Figure 3-6. Thus, the linear path indicates three cascaded amplifier stages; it could map a three-stage audio preamplifier or a three-stage IF amplifier. Next, the divergent path indicates a nonlinear circuit section followed by undefined output sections. It could represent a picture-detector section followed by an intercarrier-sound section and a video-amplifier section. Again, the convergent path indicates two separate nonlinear input sections driving an output amplifier. It could represent the outputs from two translator detectors driving a distribution amplifier in a CATV system. Finally, the convergent-divergent path indicates two separate amplifying input sections driving a full-wave bridge and followed by two separate output amplifier sections. It could represent signal paths and functional sections in a switching-bridge decoder.

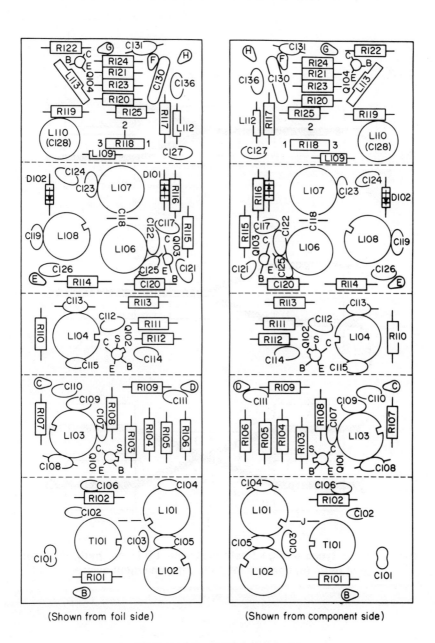

(Shown from foil side)   (Shown from component side)

Fig. 3-3   Layout diagram for a typical PC board.

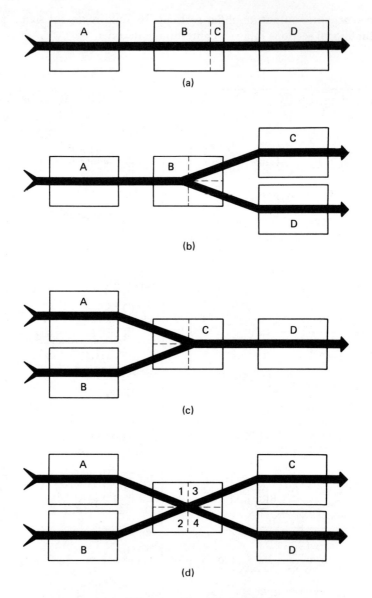

Fig. 3-4 Basic types of signal-path diagrams. (a) Linear path; (b) divergent path; (c) convergent path; (d) convergent-divergent path.

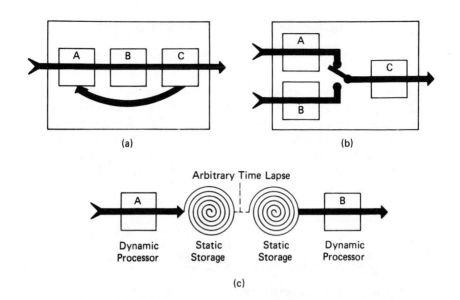

Fig. 3-5 Feedback, switching signal, and dynamic/static paths. (a) Basic negative-feedback arrangement; (b) simple switching configuration; (c) dynamic/static and static/dynamic signal paths.

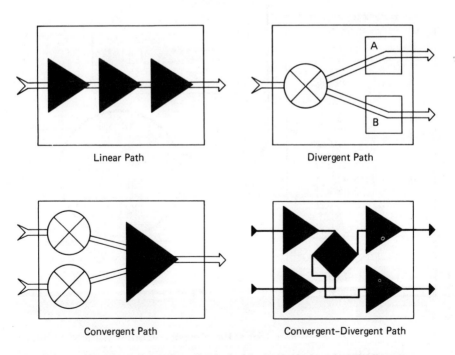

Fig. 3-6 Functional sections included in typical signal-path diagrams.

41

3-3   Picture Diagrams

Various types of picture diagrams (pictorial diagrams) are used in electronic repair and diagnosis procedures. For example, when a television receiver is to be aligned, the troubleshooter may refer to a pictorial test setup
diagram as shown in Figure 3-7. This type of diagram has an advantage in
that it is direct and straight to the point—no interpretation of symbols is required. Again, a production repairman may refer to a pictorial assembly and
wiring diagram, as exemplified in Figure 3-8. This is the same kind of dia-

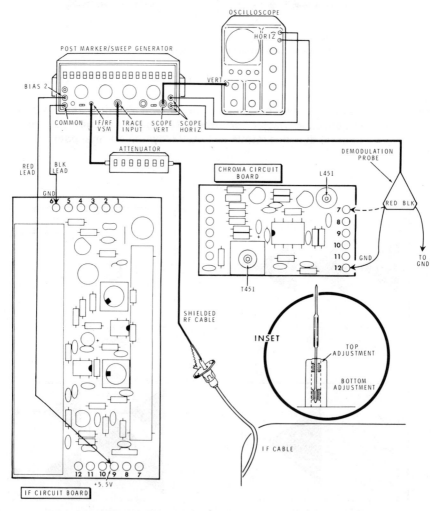

Fig. 3-7   Typical alignment test-setup pictorial diagram. (Courtesy, Heath
Co.)

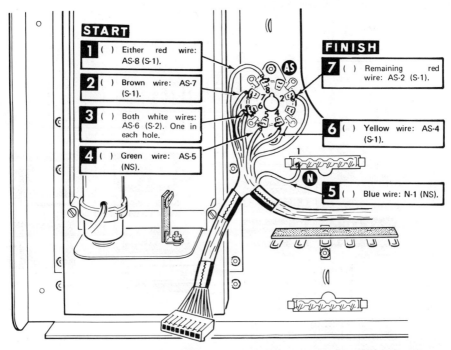

Fig. 3-8   A pictorial assembly and wiring diagram. (Courtesy, Heath Co.)

gram that is used by factory assemblers and wiremen. Wiring errors are inevitable in production procedures, although every effort is made to eliminate them. Pictorial assembly and wiring diagrams assist greatly in minimizing wiring errors. Their utility is based upon the fact that they are physically explicit; from the viewpoint of the assembler, wireman, or repairman, nothing is left to the imagination or to understanding of symbology.

3-4   Interconnection Diagrams

Another type of pictorial diagram is exemplified in Figure 3-9. This is an interconnection diagram for a hi-fi component system. It shows how each record player, tape deck, tuner, microphone, and power amplifier is connected to its correct terminals on the rear of the preamplifier. Interconnection diagrams are sometimes elaborated to indicate the proper terminals for high-level microphones and low-level microphones, and appropriate terminals for low-level phono cartridges and high-level phono cartridges. A repairman expects that a certain percentage of his calls from hi-fi enthusiasts will involve incorrect connections of one or more components to the terminal board on the rear of the amplifier. The repairman has an advantage over the usual audiophile, in that the former is experienced; he recognizes

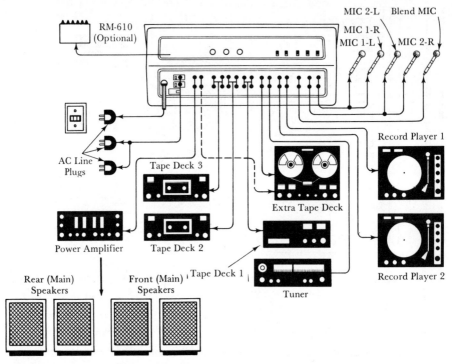

Fig. 3-9   Interconnection diagram for a hi-fi component system.

whether a particular phono cartridge or a particular microphone is a high-level type or a low-level type. A repairman is also on the alert for interconnection errors, such as confusion of tape-deck terminals with record-player terminals.

Most interconnecting cables are terminated with plugs, whereby "hot" leads cannot be accidentally confused with "ground" leads. However, this is not an invariable rule; an occasional unit will be encountered which is provided with a coaxial connecting cable terminated in spade lugs. In such a case, the interconnection diagram for the equipment may indicate the "hot" terminal and the "ground" terminal. Or, the ground terminal on the equipment may be marked "Gnd," without special identification on the interconnection diagram. This situation can lead to baffling trouble symptoms if the audiophile does not understand the distinction between the leads and accidentally cross-connects the lugs to the terminals.

3-5   Elaborated Diagrams

Diagnosticians and repairmen may refer to elaborated diagrams of various kinds. As an illustration, a block diagram in the service manual for a radio receiver may indicate the operating frequencies of the principal signal sections, with normal signal-voltage levels as exemplified in Figure 3-10. Here it is indicated that the converter section operates over a frequency range from 550 to kHz to 1500 kHz, that the IF section operates at 455 kHz, and that the audio section operates from 100 Hz to 10 kHz. It also indicates that if a 7-microvolt (7μV) input signal is applied to the converter, that the signal level will normally be stepped up to 50 millivolts (50 mV) at the output of the IF amplifier. It is understood in this situation that the carrier is amplitude-modulated 30 percent by a 1-kHz sine-wave voltage. In turn, the diagram advises the troubleshooter that an output signal level of 707 mV will be normally anticipated at the output of the audio amplifier.

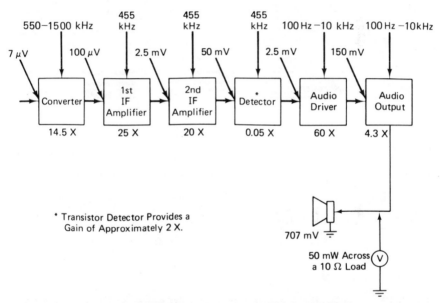

Fig. 3-10   Block diagram with signal-voltage levels and operating frequencies for a small transistor radio receiver.

Again, a schematic diagram in the service manual for a television receiver may include normal signal waveforms with peak-to-peak voltage values, with normal DC voltage values at each of the transistor terminals. A more elaborated type of diagram may specify DC voltage values both in the absence of input signal and with normal signal input applied, as exemplified in Figure 3-11. This form of elaboration can be of great assistance to the diagnostician, inasmuch as it provides significant supplementary data for preliminary analysis of malfunction. For example, suppose that C29 is open. This fault is easily located if an oscilloscope is available. On the other hand,

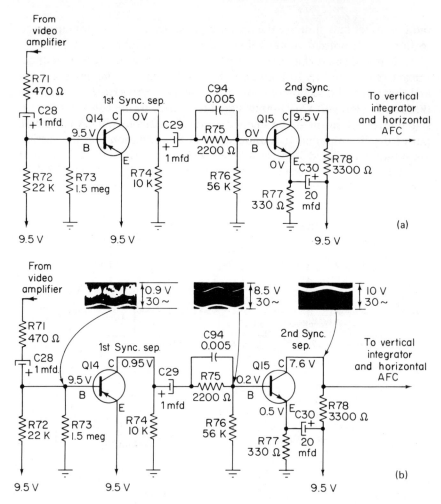

Fig. 3-11 **DC voltage distribution under no-signal and signal conditions. (a) Voltage values in absence of signal; (b) voltage values with normal signal level present.**

if an oscilloscope is not available, the fault is comparatively difficult to locate. With DC voltages specified both in the presence and in the absence of signal, it becomes possible to quickly locate the defect on the basis of DC voltage measurements.

3-6 Elaborated Block Diagrams

Preliminary malfunction diagnosis can be facilitated by reference to an elaborated block diagram such as shown in Figure 3-12. This is a color-TV

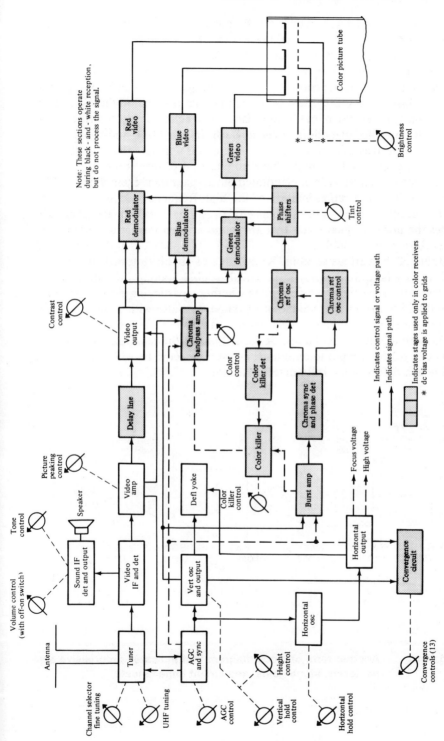

Fig. 3-12 Example of a block diagram with signal-flow, basic-function, and control-location data.

receiver arrangement in which the functional sections are indicated with distinction between chroma and black-and-white channels, signal paths are depicted, control-signal or voltage paths are included, and the section associated with each operating and maintenance control is indicated. In turn, the repairman can correlate control reactions with particular trouble symptoms. As an illustration, it is evident from the diagram that the brightness control is normally independent of the contrast control action. It is also evident that faults in the color demodulator sections can impair black-and-white reproduction as well as color reproduction. Again, it is apparent that the setting of the color control will normally have no effect on picture contrast.

Another helpful type of elaborated block diagram is exemplified in Figure 3-13. This is a representation of the high-frequency section for an FM radio receiver. It shows the sequence of functional sections, and also indicates the normal signal levels that are found at each stage, the normal gain of each stage in dB, and also the normal circuit impedances at the inputs and outputs of the various sections. Knowledge of circuit (internal) impedance values can be quite helpful in practical troubleshooting procedures, inasmuch as the repairman can determine whether a particular test instrument is suitable, both from the standpoint of range, and also with respect to input impedance or output signal level. Observe that the ratio detector in Figure 3-13 normally introduces a loss of 3 dB. Thus, if the repairman measures a loss of 8 dB from input to output of the ratio detector, he will conclude that there is a defect in the ratio-detector section.

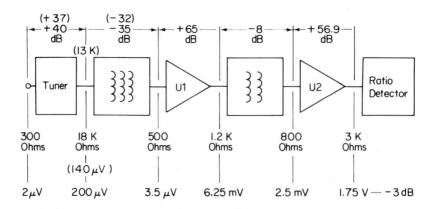

Fig. 3-13 **Another form of block diagram that indicates progressive signal levels, stage gains, and circuit impedances.**

3-7 Simplified Schematic Diagrams

Occasionally, an electronic service manual will provide skeleton schematic diagrams for complex circuitry. A skeleton schematic shows the essential signal-processing features of a circuit section and ignores nonessential details. Such skeleton diagrams are quite helpful to the repairman in diagnosing baffling trouble symptoms. In various situations, it is helpful for the troubleshooter to sketch his own simplified schematic diagrams from detailed schematic diagrams, as exemplified in Figure 3-14. This is a representation of an audio-amplifier channel that employs considerable DC coupling. In turn, a defective component or device at one point in the network can upset the DC voltage distribution in a remote branch. This "reflection" of abnormal or subnormal voltages is aggravated by the amplifying action of the transistors in successive circuits. To diagnose a widespread upset in the DC voltage distribution, it is helpful to develop a simplfied schematic diagram, as shown in Figure 3-15.

Thus, if temporary short-circuits are applied between the base and emitter terminals of each transistor, all of the transistors will normally cut off, and the simplified schematic consists of a series-parallel resistive network or "map." In the absence of DC amplification by the transistors, a faulty component or device will produce a comparatively limited upset in DC voltage distribution, and the faulty circuit branch is more easily located. A detailed analysis of the resistive network on the basis of Ohm's law is not required in practical repair procedures. In other words, although a fault near one end of the network will upset normal DC voltage values throughout, the major upset will occur at the site of the fault, owing to the lack of DC amplification. In estimating the normal anticipated voltage values, note that for practical purposes the 1-meg resistor (R73) can be ignored; similarly, the 68-kΩ resistor (R78) can be ignored; the 47-Ω resistor (R81) can be ignored; the 100-Ω resistor (R84) can be ignored; and the 16-Ω resistor (SP2) can be ignored. Thereby, rapid estimation of normal DC voltage values is facilitated.

3-8 Skeleton Schematic Diagrams

Skeleton schematic diagrams show only the functional essentials of a configuration. All incidental features, such as controls, coupling facilities, and so on, are eliminated; power sources are not represented unless they are associated with functional essentials. As an illustration, Figure 3-16 shows skeleton schematic diagrams for a bipolar transistor in the three basic amplifier configurations. The functional essentials are the input and output electrodes, voltage gain, current gain, power gain, input resistance, and out-

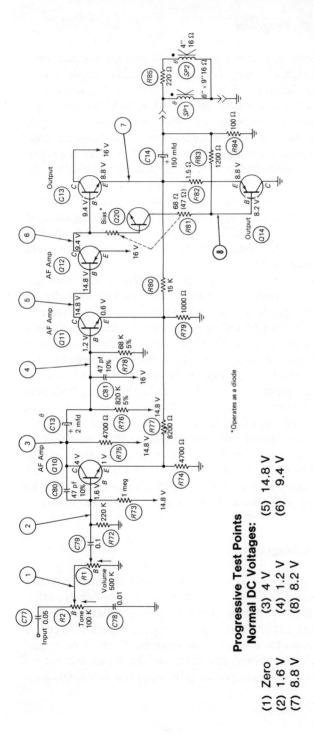

Progressive Test Points
Normal DC Voltages:

(1)	Zero	(3)	4 V	(5)	14.8 V
(2)	1.6 V	(4)	1.2 V	(6)	9.4 V
(7)	8.8 V	(8)	8.2 V		

Fig. 3-14   Audio-amplifier schematic diagram for analysis.

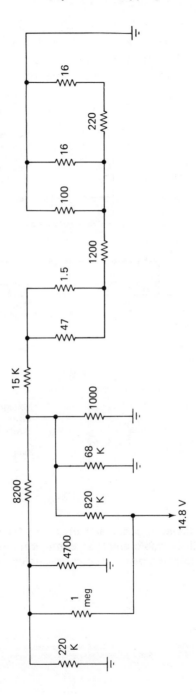

Fig. 3-15 Analytic schematic diagram (equivalent circuit) for configuration in Figure 3-14 with transistor base–emitter terminals at the same potential.

put resistance. Similarly, Figure 3-17 shows basic field-effect transistor (FET) arrangements in skeleton schematic form. The functional essentials are the input and output electrodes, voltage gain, transconductance, power gain, input resistance, and output resistance.

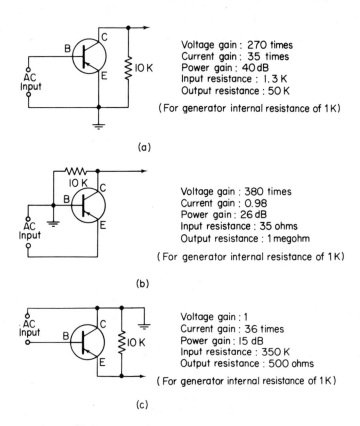

Voltage gain : 270 times
Current gain : 35 times
Power gain : 40 dB
Input resistance : 1.3 K
Output resistance : 50 K

(For generator internal resistance of 1K)

(a)

Voltage gain : 380 times
Current gain : 0.98
Power gain : 26 dB
Input resistance : 35 ohms
Output resistance : 1 megohm

(For generator internal resistance of 1K)

(b)

Voltage gain : 1
Current gain : 36 times
Power gain : 15 dB
Input resistance : 350 K
Output resistance : 500 ohms

(For generator internal resistance of 1K)

(c)

Fig. 3-16 **Skeleton schematic diagrams for a bipolar transistor in the three basic amplifier configurations. (a) Common emitter; (b) common base; (c) common collector (emitter follower).**

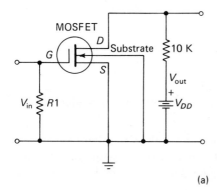

Voltage gain: 50 times
Transconductance: 5,000 μmhos
Power gain: 17 dB (50 times)
Input resistance: Very high
Output resistance: 20 K
(For generator internal resistance
of 500 Ohms)

(a)

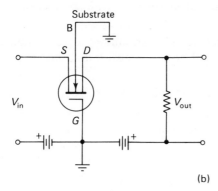

Voltage gain: 1.8 times
Input resistance: 240 Ohms)
Output resistance: High
(For generator internal
resistance of 500 Ohms)

(b)

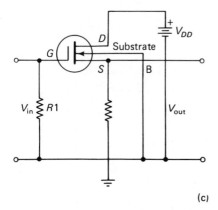

Voltage gain: 0.5
Input resistance: 2 meg
Output resistance: 240 Ohms)
(For generator internal
resistance of 500 Ohms)

(c)

Fig. 3-17 **Skeleton schematic diagrams for a field-effect transistor in the three basic amplifier configurations. (a) Common source; (b) common gate; (c) common drain (source follower).**

Review Questions

1.   What is the central purpose of a mapping technique in electronic system diagnostic procedures?
2.   Describe a signal-path diagram.
3.   Why is a pictorial diagram desirable in particular troubleshooting procedures?
4.   Give an example of an elaborated block diagram.
5.   How does a schematic diagram with specified signal/no-signal DC voltage distributions facilitate diagnosis of malfunctions?
6.   Explain the purpose of a simplified schematic diagram.
7.   When is it helpful to have a block diagram with specified signal-voltage levels?
8.   Describe a short-circuit technique for simplifying a DC-amplifier schematic diagram by causing all normal transistors to become effective open-circuits.
9.   Does a skeleton circuit diagram usually specify DC voltage values?
10.   Explain the general approach that technicians use to reduce a series-parallel resistive network to a simpler form, or to a basic equivalent circuit.

Chapter 4

Malfunction Analysis

4-1 Basic Principles

Numerous kinds of malfunctions occur in radio, television, and sound system equipment; and it often happens that a certain trouble symptom could be caused by more than one type of malfunction. Therefore, malfunction analysis is concerned with evaluation of the configuration(s) used in the receiver or other equipment, development of a list of possible malfunctions in order of probability if feasible, and then identification of the actual malfunction by diagnostic tests. Consider, for example, the trouble symptom: "dead" radio receiver. If there is no clicking sound from the speaker when the power switch is turned off and on, the fault could be in any one of the shaded blocks depicted in Figure 4-1. Thus, there may be no output voltage from the power supply (or batteries); the output stage in the audio amplifier may be open-circuited; the speaker may be open-circuited or short-circuited.

On the other hand, if there is a clicking sound from the speaker but no signal output from the speaker when the power switch is turned off and on, the receiver is analyzed in another "dead" category. That is, the clicking sound from the speaker indicates that the power supply is working, that the audio-output stage is operative, and that the speaker is alright. In turn, there is the possibility of a short-circuited antenna, a defective front end, a faulty IF amplifier, an inoperative detector, a malfunctioning AGC section, or a failed AF amplifier. Accordingly, the repairman will make an "educated guess" concerning which of these sections is most likely to be the culprit, and either confirm or eliminate the possibility by means of appropriate tests. As detailed subsequently, an "educated guess" is not necessarily made without some logical reason in this situation. In other words, preliminary quick-checks can be made to distinguish between IF, front-end, and detector-AGC trouble areas.

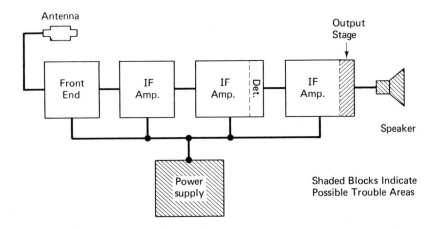

Fig. 4-1   Possible trouble areas in a completely dead radio receiver.

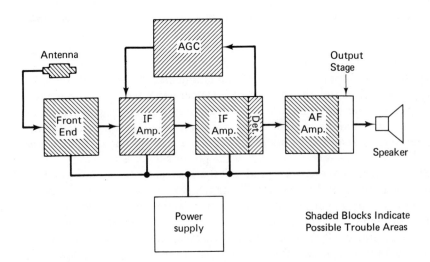

Fig. 4-2   Possible trouble areas in a radio receiver with no signal output.

4-2 Noise Output

Still another category of "dead receiver" is a radio that has noise output only. When the power switch is turned off and on, there is an audible click from the speaker; however, stations cannot be tuned in, and there is noise output only. With reference to Figure 4-3, this trouble symptom throws suspicion on the RF section of the receiver, or possibly on the antenna. Thus, the antenna could be short-circuited, or the RF amplifier could be "dead." It would be less likely that the converter is "dead" because this stage contributes a substantial proportion of the total noise output. However, this malfunction analysis is not conclusive; for instance, a noisy transistor in the AF section could cause the same trouble symptom. To distinguish between noise that originates in the RF section and noise that is produced in the AF section, the repairman turns the volume control through its range and listens for any change in noise level. If the noise disappears at low settings of the volume control, he concludes that the trouble will be found in the RF section. On the other hand, if the noise level does not respond to changes in volume-control settings, he concludes that the trouble will be found in the AF section.

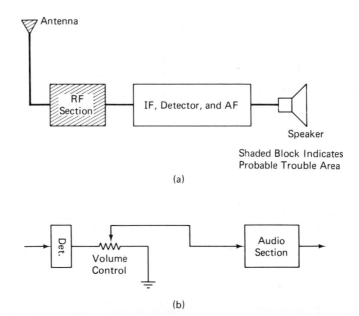

(a)

(b)

Fig. 4-3 **Probable trouble area in a radio receiver with noise output only. (a) Most of the noise is generated in the input section of the receiver; (b) volume control action provides clue to trouble localization.**

4-3 Malfunction Analysis of "Weak Output"

Analysis of a "weak output" trouble symptom is more involved than in a "dead receiver" situation. However, some preliminary malfunction analysis procedures are comparatively simple. For example, consider an AM/FM radio receiver, depicted in Figure 4-4(a). In the event that AM reception is normal and FM reception is weak, the technician turns his attention immediately to the FM section in the receiver. Conversely, if FM reception is normal and AM reception is weak, the AM section is cleared from suspicion. In case that both the AM and the FM outputs are weak, the power supply or the audio section would be checked at the outset. In the case of a multiband radio receiver, diagrammed in figure 4-4(b), the serviceman will observe whether reception may be weak on one or more of the bands, but normal on the other bands. Thus, if it is found that weak output occurs on only one of the short-wave bands, a large portion of the receiver circuitry is eliminated from suspicion.

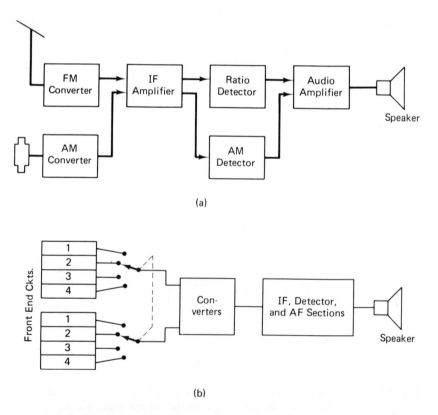

(a)

(b)

Fig. 4-4   **Radio receiver arrangements. (a) AM/FM receiver; (b) multiband receiver.**

A color-television receiver comprises four principal signal sections, as depicted in Figure 4-5. The RF and IF high-frequency section is common to the three sound, black-and-white, and chroma sections. In turn, if the black-and-white picture is weak, the color picture is weak or absent, and sound reproduction is noisy at times, the technician will suspect that there is a fault in the high-frequency section. It would also be possible that the antenna is short-circuited or disconnected. On the other hand, if the sound output is weak but the black-and-white and color picture reproduction is normal, he will conclude that there is a defect in the sound section. Or, if color reproduction is weak but black-and-white reproduction and sound output are normal, the repairman will look for a malfunction in the chroma section.

Consider next a complaint of weak output on the R channel in the stereo system depicted in Figure 4-6. The serviceman starts his diagnosis by checking the R-channel output on various functions of the system. Thus, if the R-channel output is weak on the turntable function only, he proceeds to replace the phono cartridge. On the other hand, in case that the R-channel output is weak on the FM-stereo function only, he turns his attention to the multiplex decoder. In the event that the R-channel output is weak on the tape-player function only, he proceeds to replace the playback head. Or, if the R-channel output is weak on all three functions, the technician concludes that the trouble will be found in the R-channel amplifier path (R equalizer, right-channel AF amplifier, right-channel power amplifier, or R speaker).

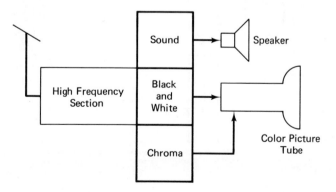

Fig. 4-5   A color-TV receiver has four principal signal sections.

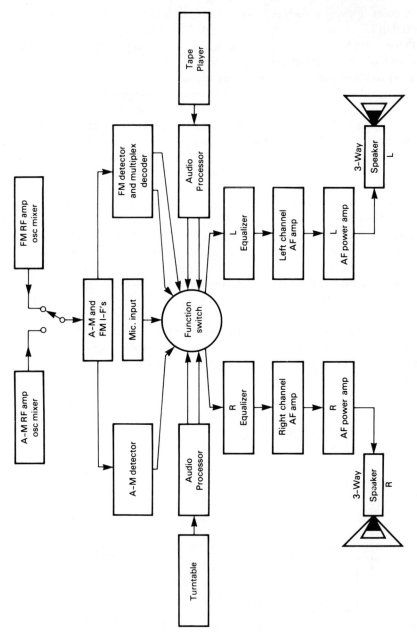

Fig. 4-6   Arrangement of a typical hi-fi stereo system.

4-4   Distorted Output Analysis

Distortion analysis is often more involved than evaluation of catastrophic failures. In other words, numerous possibilities must frequently be
considered, and comparatively small departures from normal operation may
be responsible for distortion malfunctions. Consider the tape-recorder block
diagram shown in Figure 4-7. When distorted output occurs, the audio
technician usually checks the tape first; that is, if a chromium dioxide tape is
used on a machine designed for ferromagnetic tape, both recording and reproduction will be impaired. Another type of distortion results from cross-
talk between tape tracks; in this situation, the serviceman suspects that the
playback head height may be incorrect, that the tape may be in damaged

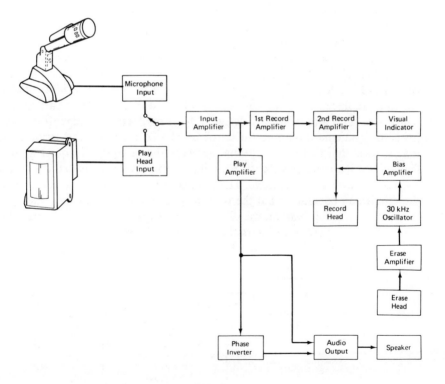

Fig. 4-7   Tape recorder block diagram for malfunction analysis.

condition, or that there may be some foreign substance in the cartridge opening. Or, if distortion involves poor high-frequency response, the repairman will suspect that the playback head is fouled with oxide deposits, that the head may be excessively worn, that the head may be misaligned, or that an amplifier stage is faulty.

In the event that distorted output is accompanied by scraping, rattling, or buzzing sounds, the technician will suspect that the speaker is defective. However, certain amplifier malfunctions can simulate a defective speaker. Hence, a speaker substitution test is usually made when this trouble symptom occurs. Distortion characterized by loud popping sounds directs suspicion to a defective voice-coil connection. In case that the complaint involves unbalanced outputs in a stereo arrangement, the serviceman will suspect that there is a weak audio-amplifier stage. However, there is also the possibility of a misadjusted balance control, incorrect height of the tape head, or a faulty tape head. Or, if the complaint concerns distortion on the recording function only, the serviceman will suspect that there may be a malfunction in the AC bias section. Of course, there is also the possibility of a defect in the recording amplifier, a worn or fouled recording head, or even a faulty microphone.

Consider next a preliminary malfunction analysis of distortion in a phono preamplifier arrangement, as depicted in Figure 4-8. Of course, suspicion is first directed to the stylus, and the technician will inspect it for excessive wear under a stylus microscope. There is also a possibility that a cartridge replacement error has been made, and that a ceramic cartridge is being used with a preamplifier designed for a magnetic cartridge. If the stylus is in good condition, and the cartridge is a correct type, the serviceman may suspect that there is an internal defect in the cartridge. To quickly confirm or eliminate this possibility, he will interchange the leads to the left and right terminals on the cartridge. Then, if distortion persists in the R channel, the repairman concludes that the trouble will be found in the amplifier circuitry. On the other hand, if the distortion now appears in the L channel, he concludes that there is an internal defect in the cartridge.

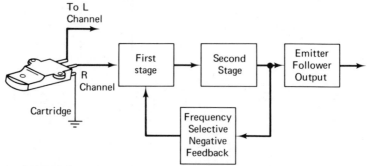

Fig. 4-8
Phono preamplifier arrangement.

4-5 Intermittent Operation Analysis

Intermittent operation is a type of malfunction that is often very difficult to analyze. A TV receiver, for example, sometimes develops an intermittent condition in the signal channel that causes the picture to disappear for a time; later, the picture reappears just as inexplicably. The technician may be able to localize the general area of malfunction by inspection of the snow level when the picture disappears. For instance, if the signal is stopped in the video detector or video amplifier, the snow level will be very low, as in Figure 4-9(a). Again, if the signal is stopped in the mixer section, a medium snow level will be displayed, as in Figure 4-9(b). Or, if the signal is stopped in the RF amplifier section, the snow level will be high, as in Figure 4-9(c). With reference to Figure 4-10, the serviceman also notes whether the sound disappears with the picture, or not. If the sound continues after the picture disappears, the trouble will be found in the picture channel following the sound-takeoff point.

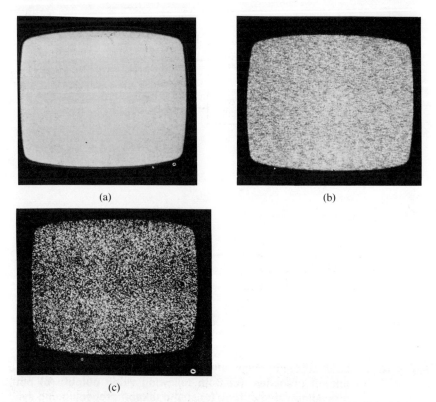

(a)　　　　　　　　　　(b)

(c)

Fig. 4-9　　Three different snow levels. (a) Low snow level; (b) medium snow level; (c) high snow level.

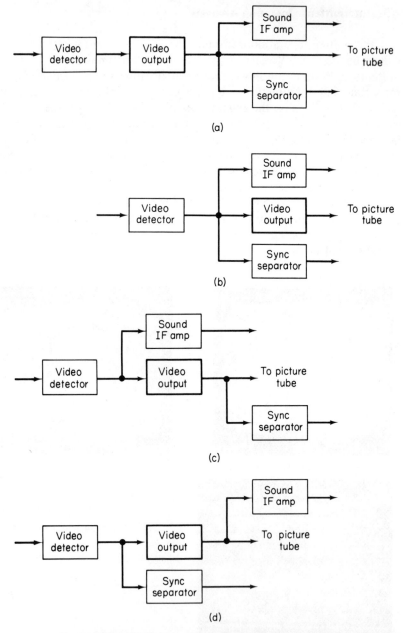

Fig. 4-10 Four different diagnostic arrangements of sound and sync takeoff branches. (a) Both following video output; (b) both preceding video output; (c) sound takeoff preceding and sync takeoff following video output; (d) sound takeoff following and sync takeoff preceding video output.

Consider next the preliminary analysis of an intermittent condition in an FM tuner, such as depicted in Figure 4-11. When reception stops, noise output may or may not be audible from the speaker; the volume control may need to be advanced. In case that the signal is being stopped in the ratio detector, the noise output will be quite low, and may be inaudible even with the volume control turned fully on. On the other hand, if the signal is stopped in the RF amplifier, the noise output will be quite audible—particularly with the volume control advanced. In the event that the signal is being stopped at an IF stage, an intermediate noise output level will be noted. Thus, an experienced repairman can make a useful preliminary diagnosis of an intermittent malfunction merely by noting the prevailing system noise level.

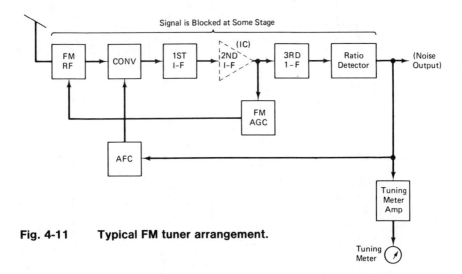

Fig. 4-11   Typical FM tuner arrangement.

When an intermittent condition occurs in a closed-circuit television camera arrangement (Figure 4-12), the troubleshooter seldom finds that the entire system "goes dead." Instead, a preliminary diagnosis usually shows that the FM sound signal drops out, or that the camera-signal component drops out from the complete video signal, or that the sync component drops out. In other intermittent situations, all of the signal components remain, but the automatic-frequency-control (AFC) action "lets go." Again, an intermittent condition may consist in the sudden onset of audio distortion, in the onset of video signal clipping, or in a sudden appearance of high-level hum or noise in the video signal or in the sound signal, or both. Thus, by careful observation of the intermittent condition, the technician can often accomplish considerable preliminary localization. This preliminary analysis requires a good understanding of system operation so that the diagnostician can reason back logically from effect (symptom) to cause (probable fault).

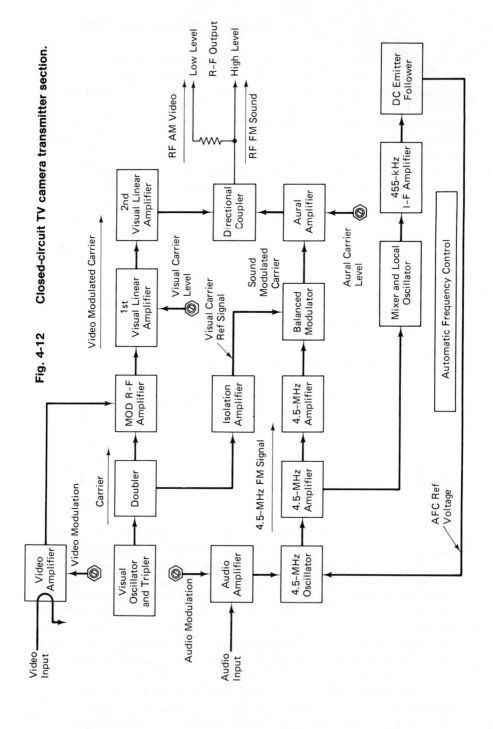

Fig. 4-12   Closed-circuit TV camera transmitter section.

66

4-6   Interference Malfunction Analysis

Interference is very common in some areas of electronic communication, as in citizen's-band radio and amateur radio reception. The first step in malfunction analysis is to determine whether the interference results from a receiver defect, or from co-channel signal interception. A comparison test with another known good receiver will distinguish between these two causes of interference. When the trouble is caused by co-channel signal reception, it is often possible to reduce or eliminate the undesired co-channel signal by means of a highly directional antenna, such as depicted in Figure 4-13. In difficult situations, further reduction in co-channel interference can usually be accomplished by employing single-sideband transmission and reception instead of double-sideband communication, as depicted in Figure 4-14.

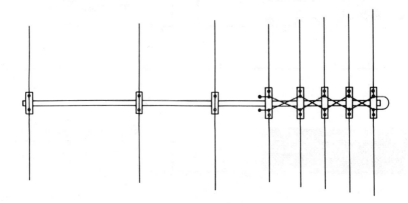

Fig. 4-13   Example of a Yagi antenna with eight elements. Note: A rotor is usually required with a Yagi antenna.

4-7   Audio Rectification

Another type of interference that may be experienced in audio equipment that is installed in an automobile is called "audio rectification." This trouble symptom appears as AM, FM, or TV program material that is reproduced by a cassette player, for example. Motor vehicles drive through regions of greatly varying RF field strength. Thus, at one time, the motorist may be driving through a tunnel where the field strength is very weak; next, he may be driving past an AM or FM or TV broadcast installation where the field strength is extremely high. In turn, any audio system in the vehicle may develop interference consisting of distorted program material. This is called

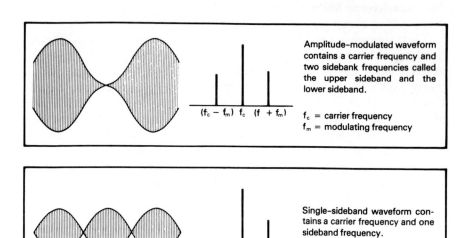

Amplitude-modulated waveform contains a carrier frequency and two sidebank frequencies called the upper sideband and the lower sideband.

$(f_c - f_m)$ f_c $(f + f_m)$

f_c = carrier frequency
f_m = modulating frequency

Single-sideband waveform contains a carrier frequency and one sideband frequency.

f_c $(f_c + f_m)$

Single-sideband waveform with suppressed carrier contains one sideband frequency.

$(f_c + f_m)$

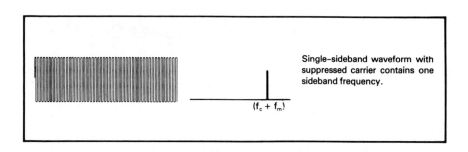

RECEPTION: The incoming single-sideband waveform with its suppressed carrier is mixed with a locally-generated carrier voltage to reconstitute the single-sideband-with-carrier waveform.

Fig. 4-14   Single sideband transmission and reception.

radio-frequency interference (RFI), and its source is "audio rectification." In other words, high-level RF energy that is picked up by a tape player or a preamp can become audible if it overdrives an audio transistor and thereby develops a rectified audio-frequency component. (See Figure 4-15.)

The first step in this type of malfunction analysis is to determine where the RFI is entering so that it can be bypassed. For instance, the RF energy

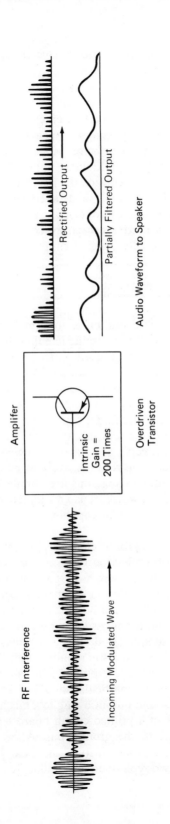

Fig. 4-15 Principle of "audio rectification."

may be entering via the power lead to the audio system—the repairman checks whether a bypass capacitor or an LC filter will reduce or eliminate the interference. Sometimes the RFI enters via the speaker leads—the technician checks whether bypassing the speaker leads will attenuate the interference. In some situations, better shielding of the audio equipment is required. If none of these preliminary approaches brings the "audio rectification" under satisfactory control, the repairman must provide adequate RF filtering in the AF circuitry, as detailed subsequently. Noise (electrical noise) interference is also a problem in various motor-vehicle audio installations. This kind of interference can be controlled by means of suitable capacitive and resistive filtering and suppressor arrangements, as explained and illustrated in the following chapter.

4-8 "Failure-Prone" Analysis

A "failure-prone" condition is not a malfunction in the strict sense of the term. Instead, it is a shortcoming in either the design or repair of a radio, television, or sound unit that results in frequent callbacks for the same trouble symptom. For instance, if there are leaky filter capacitors in the power supply of a radio, television, or sound system or receiver, the repairman is likely to have frequent callbacks to reset tripped circuit breakers—until the leaky capacitors are replaced. Of course, circuit breakers can be tripped by an abnormal current demand in any of the branch circuits from a power supply. Note that it is very poor practice to defeat a circuit breaker by short-circuiting the device—the result is likely to be catastrophic damage to the equipment, or possibly a dangerous fire. Similarly, fused equipment should never be overfused; however, it is considered permissible to install slow-blow fuses with rated current capability to avoid blowing due to starting current surges.

It is sometimes helpful to check supplementary service data issued by the manufacturer of a televison receiver, for example, when frequent callbacks occur. As an illustration, a design shortcoming in a particular model of color-TV receiver resulted in short life-expectancy for the high-voltage rectifier/multiplier. After a period of field experience, the manufacturer recognized the design fault and issued supplementary service data noting the availability of an adequately designed rectifier/multiplier for servicemen. After this model of receiver was repaired with the newly designed component, it was no longer "failure-prone" and had normal reliability potential. As another illustration, a particular model of TV receiver was found to develop intermittent sound output owing to a mechanical design shortcoming. A rivet at the edge of a printed-circuit board tended to corrode and make intermittent contact to the ground bus. After the manufacturer became aware of this "failure-prone" feature, the factory issued supplementary service data that advised repairmen to install a "jumper" connection to ground over the failure path when this particular model of receiver came into a shop for any reason.

4-9 Elimination of "Phantom Faults"

Note that good components and devices are sometimes needlessly replaced because the troubleshooter has been misled by a "phantom fault" in his general approach to the problem. Almost every trouble symptom has more than one possible cause. Each possibility must be carefully evaluated from the viewpoint of receiver or equipment performance and of electrical measurements. With sufficient information to consider, logical reasoning will serve to eliminate the "phantom faults" and to identify definitely the real fault. Of course, the general approach must take all possible causes into account; experience counts in this regard, and even the seasoned troubleshooter may overlook a possible (and real) cause of malfunction on occasion.

Review Questions

1. What is the purpose of diagnostic tests in preliminary troubleshooting procedures?
2. How does the noise output from a "dead" radio receiver sometimes provide trouble localization clues?
3. Explain the first test that should be made on a malfunctioning AM/FM radio receiver.
4. Why is a "distorted output" trouble symptom more involved than a "dead receiver" condition?
5. Describe a practical analysis of the snow level on the screen of a TV receiver with a raster-but-no-picture trouble symptom.
6. How can co-channel interference be reduced in CB radio reception?
7. Describe the general characteristics of "audio rectification."
8. Suggest a probable cause of repetitive circuit-breaker tripping in a line-powered unit of electronic equipment.
9. When would it be advisable to check for supplementary service data issued by a television receiver manufacturer?
10. Give a simple example of a "phantom fault."

Chapter 5
Hi-Fi Stereo System Repair

5-1 General Survey

Audio malfunction diagnosis includes signal-tracing tests, signal-substitution tests, frequency-response checks, transient-response tests, distortion measurements, power-bandwidth measurements, power-output tests, separation measurements, and related tests as summarized in Table 5-1. Each basic type of diagnostic test includes various subclassifications; for instance, distortion tests are subclassified into total harmonic distortion (THD) measurements, intermodulation (IM) distortion measurements, and transient intermodulation (TIM) distortion measurements. Several varieties of harmonic and intermodulation distortion are categorized as crossover, stretching, changeover, clipping, compression, expansion, and recovery distortion. Basic audio tests can be classified into steady-state responses and transient-state responses, although it will be found that a sharp dividing line cannot be drawn between them in some instances. Steady-state responses are fundamentally determined with a sine-wave signal source. On the other hand, transient-state response may be determined with respect to square-wave, pulse, or tone-burst signal sources. Transient intermodulation distortion is determined with respect to a combined square-wave and sine-wave signal. (See Figure 5-1.)

Gain measurements include voltage-gain and power-gain values; current-gain values are generally restricted to amplifying devices. Power gain can be expressed as a watt ratio or in terms of decibels (dB). Voltage gain can also be expressed in dB. Power-gain dB values are meaningful regard-

Table 5-1   Diagnostic Audio Tests and Measurements

1. **Signal-tracing tests; generator or other signal source**
   a. Oscilloscope
   b. Signal tracer
   c. Audio voltmeter
2. **Signal substitution tests; generator or other signal source**
   a. AM/FM generator
   b. Noise generator
   c. Hum injection
3. **Frequency-response checks; generator signal source**
   a. Oscilloscope
   b. Audio voltmeter
   c. Audio wattmeter
4. **Transient-response tests; square-wave, pulse, or burst signal source**
   a. Oscilloscope
   b. XY plotter
   c. Spectrum analyzer
5. **Distortion measurements; audio generator or two-tone generator**
   a. Harmonic distortion meter
   b. Intermodulation analyzer
   c. Spectrum analyzer
6. **Power-bandwidth measurements; audio generator signal source**
   a. Oscilloscope
   b. Audio voltmeter
   c. Audio wattmeter
7. **Power-output tests; audio generator signal source**
   a. Audio wattmeter
   b. Oscilloscope
   c. Harmonic distortion meter (supplementary)
8. **Separation measurements; stereo signal source**
   a. Decibel meter(s)
   b. Oscilloscope
   c. Audio voltmeter
9. **DC voltage measurements**
   a. Check measured values against specified values in equipment service data to localize faulty devices or components
   b. Check for shift in DC voltage level at collector of class-A stage with and without signal (distortion quick-test)
   c. Capacitor leakage quick-check—connect suspected capacitor in series with DC voltmeter and supply-voltage source
10. **Resistance measurements**
    a. Check measured values against specified values in equipment service data to localize faulty components
    b. Measure values of many resistors in-circuit with a lo-pwr ohmmeter—lo-pwr ohmmeter does not turn on semiconductor junctions
    c. Check diode or transistor junctions for front-to-back ratio with a hi-pwr ohmmeter—a substantial front-to-back ratio shows that the junction is workable

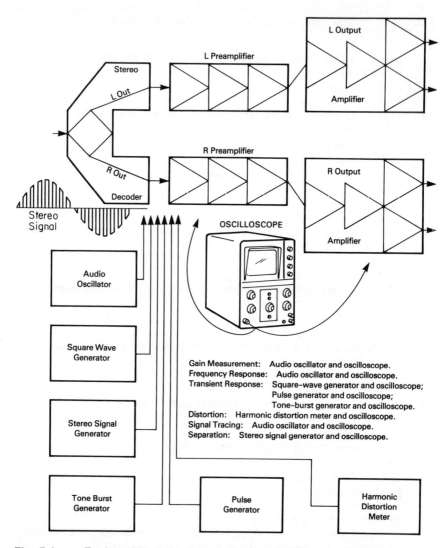

Fig. 5-1   Equipment used in basic audio tests and measurements.

less of circuit impedances. On the other hand, voltage-gain or current-gain dB values become meaningful only when evaluated with respect to circuit impedances. As shown in Figure 5-2, a high-fidelity amplifier includes a preamplifier section and a power-amplifier section. Although the preamplifier is also a power amplifier, it operates at a comparatively low power level. A unit comprising a preamplifier and a power amplifier is called an integrated amplifier. A power gain of 47 dB is typical for a preamplifier, and 38

Fig. 5-2   A good-quality stereo amplifier. (Courtesy, Radio Shack)

dB for a power amplifier, with a total power gain of 85 dB. This is called the amplifier's maximum usable gain (MUG). An amplifier system also has a maximum available gain (MAG); however, this MAG value is subject to objectionable distortion. Each of the four input ports in the diagram has a rated frequency response and a rated sensitivity. Its sensitivity denotes the minimum value of input signal required to produce the rated power output. Classes of amplifier operation are noted in Table 5-2.

Table 5-2   Amplifier Classes and Transfer Modes

Class A	Linear Transfer Mode: Output waveform is the same as the input waveform (except for residual harmonic distortion) over 360 degrees of the operating cycle.
Modified Class A	Nonlinear Transfer Mode: An expansion amplifier develops an output waveform in which higher signal amplitudes are processed at higher amplification factors than are lower signal amplitudes.
Modified Class A	Nonlinear Transfer Mode: A compression amplifier develops an output waveform in which higher signal amplitudes are processed at lower amplification factors than are lesser signal amplitudes.
Class AB	Output waveform is the same as the input waveform (except for residual harmonic distortion) over 180 degrees of the operating cycle. A small amount of forward bias is used to minimize crossover distortion; class AB stages are operated in push-pull. Class AB amplifiers are usually designed with a linear transfer mode, but may be operated with expansion or compression transfer characteristics.
Class B	Output waveform is the same as the input waveform (except for residual distortion) over 180 degrees of the operating cycle. Class B stages are operated in push-pull. Class B amplifiers are usually designed with a linear transfer mode, but may be operated with expansion or compression transfer characteristics.

Class C   Output waveform is not the same as the input waveform. The output waveform occurs over less than 180 degrees of the operating cycle. Class C operation in a high-fidelity amplifier is a symptom of stage malfunction.

Class D   Output waveform is the same as the input waveform (except for residual distortion) over 360 degrees of the operating cycle. Technically, a class D amplifier differs from a class A amplifier in that the input waveform is converted into a pulse-modulated form prior to amplification and is then reconstituted into original form following amplification. Class D amplifiers are usually designed with a linear transfer mode, but may be operated with expansion or compression transfer characterlstics.

Class G   Output waveform is the same as the input waveform (except for residual distortion) over 360 degrees of the operating cycle. A class G amplifier differs from a class A amplifier in that it has a bilevel type of operation. Signal amplitudes up to a medium level are amplified by the first-level section of the amplifier; signal amplitudes above the medium level are amplified by the second-level section of the amplifier. Outputs from the two sections are combined to reconstitute the original waveform. Class G amplifiers are usually designed with a linear transfer mode, but may be operated with expansion or compression transfer characteristics.

Class H   Output waveform is the same as the input waveform (except for residual distortion) over 360 degrees of the operating cycle. A class H amplifier differs from a class A amplifier in that it operates with a variable-level power supply. When processing a low-level signal, the amplifier operates with a low supply voltage; when processing a high-level signal, the supply voltage for the amplifier automatically increases as required in order to exceed the amplitude of the signal that is being processed. Class H amplifiers are usually designed with a linear transfer mode, but may be operated with expansion or compression transfer characteristics.

5-2 Distortion Checks

A good quality stereo amplifier is illustrated in Figure 5-2. A helpful preliminary distortion test is made with an audio generator and oscilloscope, as shown in Figure 5-3. The output from a sine-wave generator is applied to the input of the amplifier under test. A power-type resistor of rated load value is connected across the output terminals of the amplifier. An oscilloscope is connected with its vertical-input terminals across the load resistor and with its horizontal-input terminals across the amplifier input terminals. A basic test is made at a frequency of 1 kHz, and the amplifier is driven to maximum rated output. Note that the rms power output is equal to E^2/R,

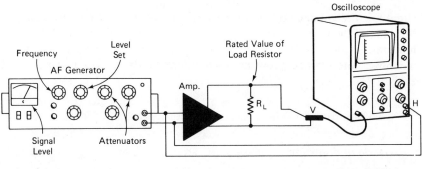

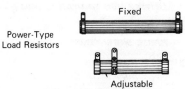

A. No overload distortion, no phase shift.
B. Overload distortion, no phase shift.
C. Driving into saturation and past cutoff, no phase shift.
D. Phase shift.
E. Overload distortion and phase shift.
F. Phase shift, driving into cutoff, and into saturation.
G. Crossover distortion, no phase shift.
H. Parasitic distortion and phase shift.
I. Parasitic distortion, no phase shift.
J. Stretching distortion, no phase shift.
K. Amplitude nonlinearity.
L. Amplitude nonlinearity with phase shift.
M. Thermal hysteresis.
N. Hum voltage in output.
O. High noise level in output.
P. One half of push-pull amplifier dead.
Q. One half of push-pull amplifier dead.
R. Unsymmetrical output waveform with phase shift.

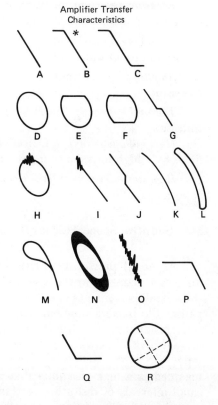

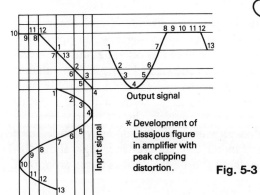

Output signal

* Development of Lissajous figure in amplifier with peak clipping distortion.

Fig. 5-3   Typical distorted amplifier-output Lissajous figures.

where E is the voltage applied to the vertical channel of the scope, and R is the value of the load resistor. A Lissajous pattern is displayed, and its shape indicates various kinds of distortion. Note that crossover distortion, hum, and noise interference show up more prominently at low power output levels.

Common causes of these forms of distortion are as follows:

Overload distortion, no phase shift. Transistor bias voltage incorrect.

Driving into saturation and past cutoff, no phase shift. Input signal voltage is excessive.

Phase shift. Phase shift at a 1-kHz test frequency points to a defective capacitor.

Crossover distortion, no phase shift. Insufficient forward-bias voltage on push-pull output transistors.

Parasitic distortion, no phase shift. This malfunction is most likely to result from an incorrect replacement type of transistor.

Stretching distortion, no phase shift. Excessive forward-bias voltage on a push-pull output transistor.

Amplitude nonlinearity. Most likely to be caused by a marginal transistor.

Thermal hysteresis. Check for an incorrect type of replacement diode or transistor.

Hum voltage in output. Defective power-supply filter, or pickup of stray fields by a high-impedance input circuit.

High noise level in output. Usually caused by a transistor with a leaky collector junction.

5-3 Sensitive Scope Test for Distortion

As noted previously, Lissajous patterns provide useful preliminary diagnostic data. However, conventional Lissajous patterns do not clearly show small percentages of distortion. Therefore it is often helpful for the repairman to make a supplementary test as shown in Figure 5-4 to enhance small residual pattern distortions and thereby make them more visible. This arrangement employs a differentiating circuit in series with the vertical-input lead to the oscilloscope. In the first analysis, the RC section may be regarded as a high-pass filter that provides a high-frequency boost. Since small intervals of distortion correspond to comparatively high audio frequencies, this filter action makes these short irregularities more prominent in the screen pattern.

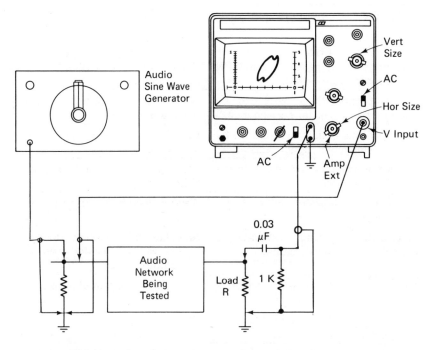

Fig. 5-4   **Sensitive oscilloscope check for harmonics in an audio waveform. (Courtesy, B&K Precision, Division of Dynascan Corp.)**

5-4   Errors in Repair Procedures

Almost every technician has made an error in repair procedure at one
time or another. As an illustration, a replacement transistor may be connected into its circuit with emitter and collector terminals interchanged. A
0.01-μF capacitor may be mistakenly replaced with a 0.001-μF capacitor. A
1-kilohm resistor may be replaced with a 1-megohm resistor. A PNP transistor may be replaced with an NPN transistor. An electrolytic capacitor
may be connected into its circuit with wrong polarity. A metal-film resistor
may be replaced with a carbon resistor. A bias diode may be connected into
its circuit with wrong polarity. A field-effect transistor may be mistakenly
replaced with a bipolar transistor. A germanium transistor may be erro-
neously replaced with a silicon transistor. Such errors in repair procedures
result in malfunctions and trouble symptoms that are usually different from
the original trouble symptoms and can lead to baffling "tough-dog" situations. Table 5-3 summarizes common errors in repair procedures and resulting trouble symptoms.

Table 5-3 Component and Device Replacement Errors

Error	Trouble Symptom
PNP transistor is replaced with NPN transistor (or vice versa).	Stage is dead; replacement transistor may burn out.
Coupling capacitor is replaced by one that has a smaller capacitance.	Low-frequency response of amplifier is impaired.
Collector load resistor is replaced by one that has much higher resistance.	High-frequency response of amplifier is impaired.
Transistor collector and emitter terminals are reversed.	Stage gain is reduced to one-half in a typical configuration.
Germanium transistor is replaced with silicon transistor.	Serious distortion and low stage gain.
Electrolytic coupling capacitor is connected in wrong polarity.	Amplifier performance deteriorates rapidly with decreasing gain and increasing distortion.
Metal film resistor in preamplifier is replaced with a carbon resistor.	Abnormal noise output from amplifier.
Field-effect transistor is replaced with a bipolar transistor.	Stage is dead.
Bias diode is connected in wrong polarity.	Severe distortion and low stage gain.
Silicon bias diode is replaced with a germanium diode.	Low stage gain and severe distortion.

5-5 Harmonic-Distortion Meter

Although percentage distortion values can be calculated from Lissajous patterns, the procedure is comparatively involved. Even if a digital calculator is used, the basic equations are complex. Accordingly, Lissajous figures are used chiefly to determine whether substantial distortion is present and the type of distortion that is involved. Precise measurements of percentage distortion values are made with a harmonic distortion meter, as depicted in

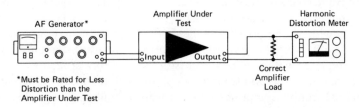

Fig. 5-5 Measurement of percentage of harmonic distortion.

Figure 5-5. A harmonic-distortion meter filters out the test frequency from the amplifier output signal but passes any harmonic frequencies that may be present. In turn, the percentage of harmonics is indicated by the meter. It is often advantageous to connect an oscilloscope at the output of the har-monic-distortion meter to display the distortion products and thereby aid in their identification. When the measured percentage of distortion exceeds the rated value for the amplifier, the repairman looks for off-value components or marginal devices in the amplifier network.

5-6 Intermodulation-Distortion Meter

Intermodulation distortion is related to harmonic distortion in that both are caused by amplitude nonlinearity in an amplifier. However, an intermod-ulation-distortion test involves a two-tone test signal instead of a single sine-wave signal (see Figure 5-6). The test is based on generation of sum and difference frequencies in nonlinear circuitry. A two-tone test signal typi-cally consists of 60-Hz and 6-kHz sine waves. Although percentages of har-monic distortion and intermodulation distortion for an amplifier are generally comparable, there is usually some difference in their measured values, particularly at very high and at very low harmonic-distortion test frequencies. When the measured percentage of intermodulation distortion exceeds the rated value for an amplifier, the repairman looks for off-value components or marginal devices in the amplifier.

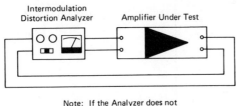

Note: If the Analyzer does not
have a Built-in Load Resistor,
use an External Load Resistor.

Fig. 5-6   Measurement of percentage intermodulation distortion.

5-7 Frequency-Response Measurements

High-fidelity sound reproduction requires adequate system frequency response. A typical system comprises a preamplifier, a power amplifier, and a speaker. Preamplifiers do not have uniform frequency response, except through the tuner input channel, as shown in Figure 5-7. Phono and tape input channels provide a substantial low-frequency boost to equalize stan-dard recording characteristics. On the other hand, power amplifiers nor-mally have uniform (flat) frequency response from 20 Hz to 20 kHz, and

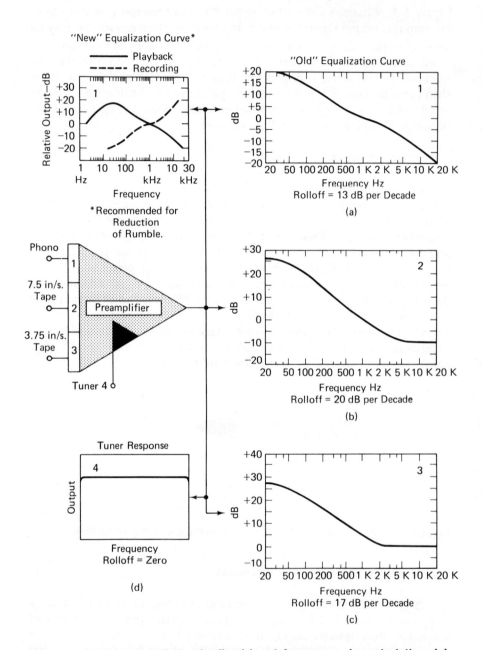

Fig. 5-7 **Examples of standardized input frequency characteristics. (a) RIAA equalization curve for playback of records; (b) NAB standard playback curve for 7.5 in./sec tape; (c) MRIA playback curve for 3.75 in./sec tape; (d) tuner response curve is flat.**

may have extended uniform frequency response from zero frequency (DC) to 100 kHz, for example. An amplifier frequency-response test setup is depicted in Figure 5-8. The amplifier is energized by an audio generator. An oscilloscope or TVM, or both, may be connected across the amplifier load resistor. An oscilloscope has the advantage of indicating whether visible distortion may be present; a TVM has the advantage of indication in both voltage and decibel units. A basic frequency-response curve is checked with the amplifier driven to its maximum rated power output at 1 kHz.

The gain of an amplifier can be checked at the same time that its frequency response is measured. Typical high-fidelity amplifier system characteristics are noted in Figure 5-9. The preamplifier operates at an input level as low as 350 μV and develops an output level of 1 V; the power amplifier steps up the 1-V input to an 8-V output level. The total system power gain is 85 dB. Subnormal gain is ordinarily caused by deteriorated devices, although faulty components can also be responsible. The same faults that result in subnormal gain can also impair the frequency response of an amplifier. With reference to Figure 5-10, power amplifiers are often rated for power bandwidth, in addition to 1-dB bandwidth at maximum rated power output. In this example, a reference distortion value of 1 percent is stipulated. The 1-dB bandwidth rating extends from f_A to f_B, which represent the low and high frequency limits of amplitude variation within 1 dB from the amplitude value at 1 kHz with maximum rated power output.

Next, the power-bandwidth rating of the amplifier extends from f_1 to f_2 where f_1 and f_2 represent the high and low frequency limits along the response curve within which the harmonic distortion does not exceed 1 percent (in this example) at 70.7 percent of maximum rated power output. Note that when the power output from an amplifier is reduced to 70.7 percent of its maximum rated value, the percentage distortion at 1 kHz decreases. However, as the low-frequency end of the response curve is approached, there is found a low-frequency limit at which the harmonic distortion will have risen to 1 percent. Similarly, as the high-frequency end of the response curve is approached, there is found a frequency limit at which the harmonic distortion will have risen to 1 percent. These two frequency limits define the power bandwidth of the amplifier.

5-8   Tone-Burst Tests

Tone-burst tests are essentially transient diagnoses and are in the category of square-wave checks. However, a tone-burst waveform has incidental steady-state intervals. Speakers are ordinarily checked for transient response by tone-burst tests. It is good practice to employ an anechoic chamber, as indicated in Figure 5-11, in order to avoid the interfering action of acoustic reflections. It is general practice to make tone-burst tests at frequencies of 100, 1000, and 10,000 Hz. Typical oscilloscope screen displays for tone-burst

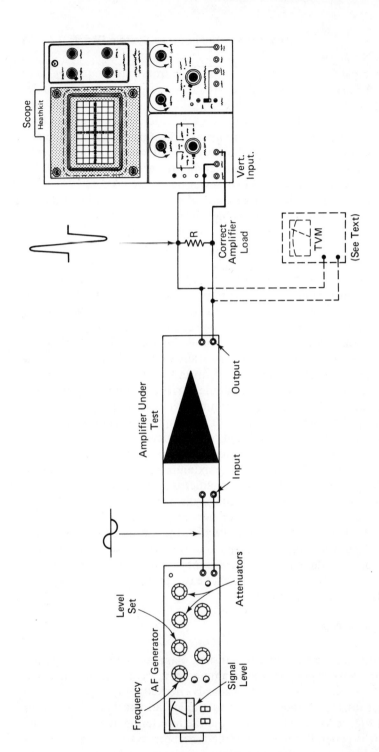

Fig. 5-8   Amplifier frequency response test setup.

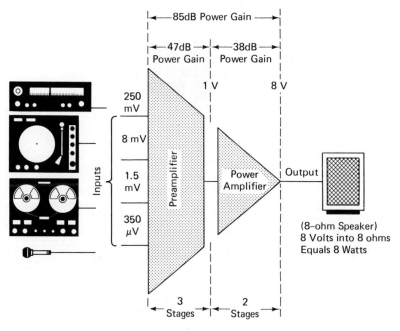

Fig. 5-9 **Typical high-fidelity amplifier system characteristics.**

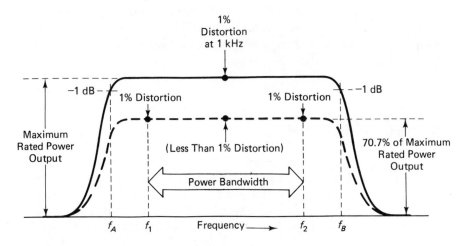

Fig. 5-10 **An example of amplifier power bandwidth.**

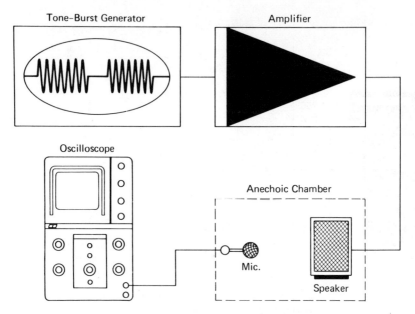

Fig. 5-11   Tone-burst test of speaker performance.

characteristics of a good-quality speaker are shown in Figure 5-12. At 100 Hz, the rise interval is slightly slowed and there is a small "hangover." At 100 Hz, there is also a tendency to some top and bottom curvature in the reproduced waveform; at 10 kHz, a low-amplitude "hangover ripple" persists between successive bursts.

5-9   Stereo Separation Tests

One of the most common trouble symptoms in an FM stereo system is poor separation. This term means that when an L signal is applied to the stereo-multiplex decoder, the sound output is not restricted to the L speaker, as it would be in ideal operation. Similarly when an R signal is applied to the decoder, the sound output is not restricted to the R speaker. Generally, a separation of 30 dB should be provided between the L and R channels by a good decoder. The basic plan of an FM stereo system is depicted in Figure 5-13. Multiplexed L and R signals are applied to the decoder which in turn separates the L and R wave envelopes and feeds them to the respective L and R amplifiers. Poor separation is commonly caused by deteriorated semiconductors in the decoder circuitry; drift in component values that produce unbalanced circuit branches can also cause this malfunction.

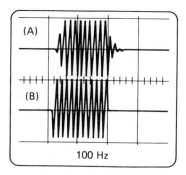

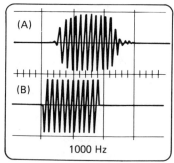

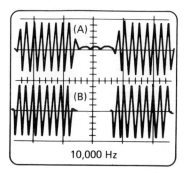

Fig. 5-12
Typical speaker tone-burst test results. (a) Acoustic output waveform produced by speaker; (b) tone-burst waveform applied to speaker. (Courtesy, Radio Shack)

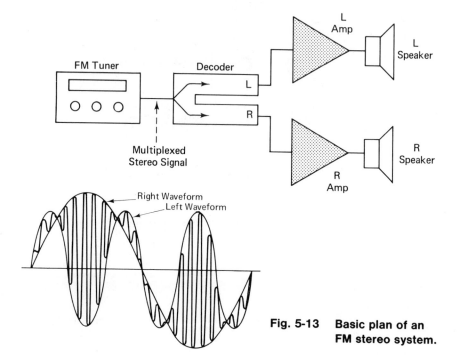

Fig. 5-13   Basic plan of an FM stereo system.

Several types of separation tests may be made. A widely used method is shown in Figure 5-14. Here, an FM stereo receiver is driven with an L signal, and then with an R signal from a stereo analyzer. Outputs from the L and R speakers are applied to a pair of dB meters built into the analyzer. Thus, the meters indicate the number of dB separation when an L signal or an R signal is applied to the receiver. In the complete absence of separation, the meters will indicate the same reading simultaneously, whether an L signal or an R signal is applied to the receiver. In other words, the separation is zero in this situation, and reproduction is monophonic. Manufacturers usually rate FM stereo receivers for normal separation. In the absence of specifications, the repairman customarily looks for a separation of about 30 dB.

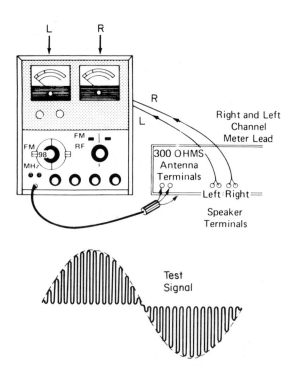

Fig. 5-14   **Stereo separation test with a stereo analyzer. (Courtesy, Sencore)**

5-10 Quick-Checks in Audio Circuitry

A useful quick test that requires only a test lead with needle-pointed prods is called a "click" test, as depicted in Figure 5-15. This test indicates whether a stage is workable. The test prods are applied to the base and emitter terminals of each transistor in turn, temporarily short-circuiting these terminals together. The speaker serves as an indicator. If the test produces a click in the speaker output, it is concluded that the section of amplifier between the test point and the speaker is workable. This test is based on the transient voltage that is generated by the temporary short circuit of the forward-bias voltage between the base and emitter terminals of the transistor.

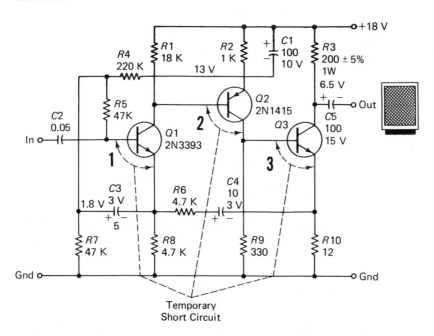

Fig. 5-15 Click tests are made by temporarily short-circuiting the base and emitter terminals of a transistor.

When there is objectionable noise output from an amplifier, a quick-check can be made as shown in Figure 5-16. A 0.1-μF capacitor is temporarily shunted across a suspected component or device. Then, if the noise level drops substantially or disappears, the repairman concludes that the noise voltages are being partially or completely suppressed due to the bypassing action of the capacitor. Note that noise generated in the early stages is amplified by subsequent stages and is more objectionable than noise generated in the later stages. It is good practice to turn the amplifier off each time before the test capacitor is connected into or disconnected from the amplifier circuitry, also to discharge the capacitor each time that it is removed from the circuit. These precautions prevent possible surge damage to semiconductor devices in the amplifier network. Noise voltages are most likely to originate in a transistor with a leaky junction, or in deteriorated base bias resistors.

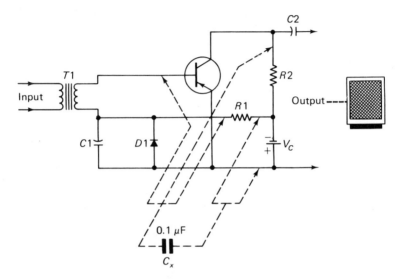

Fig. 5-16   **Noise sources can be localized by shunting components or devices with a capacitor.**

5-11   Transistor Turn-on and Turn-off Tests

Quick checks of transistor workability can be made in-circuit with a voltmeter and a test lead with needle-pointed prods (or clips) as depicted in Figure 5-17. These turn-off and turn-on tests indicate whether a transistor has normal control action. In Figure 5-17(a), a turn-off test is made by connecting a DC voltmeter between the collector terminal of a transistor and ground. When the transistor's base and emitter terminals are temporarily short-circuited together, the voltmeter reading will normally jump up to the supply-voltage value (−9 volts). If the meter reading is subnormal or remains unchanged, the transistor does not have normal control action. In (b), a similar turn-off test is shown for a negative-ground configuration. Turn-off tests are based on the fact that a bipolar transistor normally cuts off when its base and emitter terminals are brought to the same potential (zero bias).

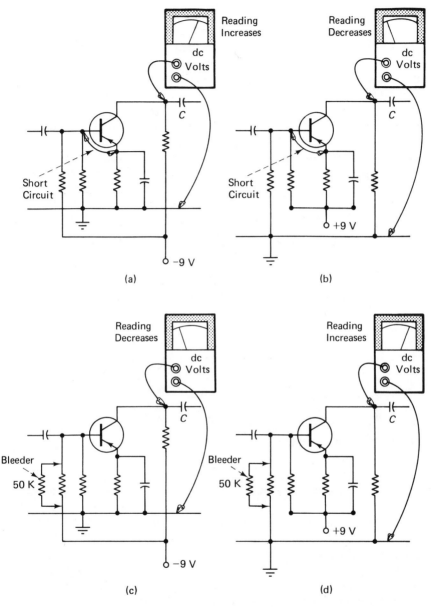

Fig. 5-17 Turn-off and turn-on tests in positive-ground and negative-ground configurations. (a) Turn-off test in a positive-ground system; meter reading increases; (b) turn-off test in a negative-ground system; meter reading decreases; (c) turn-on test in a positive-ground system; meter reading decreases; (d) turn-on test in a negative-ground system; meter reading increases.

Next, a turn-on test is made as exemplified in Figure 5-17(c). The DC voltmeter is connected between the collector terminal of a transistor and ground. When a 50-kilohm resistor is temporarily connected between the transistor's base terminal and the supply line, the voltmeter reading will normally decrease. If the meter reading does not respond to this bias change, the transistor does not have normal control action. In (d), a similar turn-on test is shown for a positive-ground configuration. In this case, the meter reading normally increases when additional bias current is bled into the transistor's base. A turn-off test can be made in a grounded-collector configuration, as shown in Figure 5-18. The voltmeter indicates the voltage drop across the emitter resistor, and the meter reading normally drops to zero when a short-circuit is applied between the transistor's base and emitter terminals.

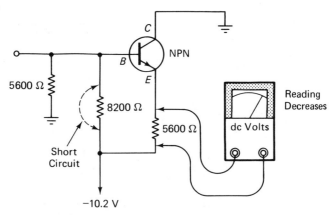

Fig. 5-18   Turn-off test in a grounded-collector configuration.

In various configurations, the base bias resistor is connected to the collector of the transistor, as exemplified in Figure 5-19. In this situation, a turn-off test is made by temporarily slitting the printed-circuit conductor that connects R1 to the transistor's base terminal. Thereby, the bias conductor is open-circuited so that the base and emitter assume the same potential. Accordingly, the meter reading jumps up to the supply-voltage value if the transistor has normal control action. After the test is completed, the slit through the PC conductor is repaired with a small drop of solder.

A turn-off test can be made in the Darlington configuration as shown in Figure 5-20. Both of the base-emitter short circuits are applied simultaneously. In turn, both transistors normally cut off, and the emitter current flow stops. Consequently, the meter reading normally drops to zero. A crosscheck is made by removing the base-emitter short circuit from Q1 first. The meter reading should remain at zero. A second crosscheck is made by removing the base-emitter short circuit from Q2, noting the meter reading, and then temporarily short-circuiting the base-emitter terminals of Q1. The meter reading normally increases. Otherwise, the stage lacks normal control action and the transistors should be replaced.

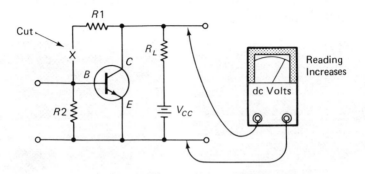

Fig. 5-19   Making a turn-off test by opening the bias circuit.

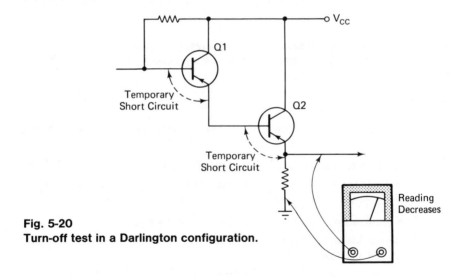

Fig. 5-20
Turn-off test in a Darlington configuration.

5-12   Transistor Curve Tracer

The most comprehensive test of a transistor is made with a transistor curve tracer. This is an instrument that applies normal operating potentials to a transistor in an out-of-circuit test. The base bias voltage is automatically passed through a series of steps, and the collector voltage is swept from zero to maximum at each bias step. In turn, the collector potential is applied to the vertical-input channel of an oscilloscope. A family of collector characteristic curves is displayed on the oscilloscope screen, as pictured in Figure 5-21. The display may be compared with the manufacturer's specified characteristics, if desired. Observe in Figure 5-21(b) that when the transistor has collector leakage, its gain is only a fraction of normal, and the characteristics become nonlinear. In the event that the transistor had zero gain, only a horizontal line would be displayed on the oscilloscope screen.

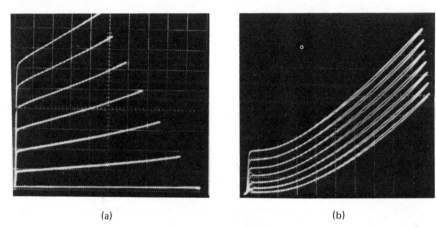

(a)   (b)

Fig. 5-21   **Typical collector-family displays. (a) Transistor in good condition; (b) transistor with excessive collector-junction leakage.**

Review Questions

1. Name several types of tests used in malfunction diagnosis of hi-fi stereo systems.
2. Why is an oscilloscope a better signal-tracing indicator than a TVM?
3. What advantage does a lo-pwr ohmmeter provide in resistance measurements when diagnosing faults in solid-state circuitry?
4. Distinguish between voltage gain and power gain.
5. How are Lissajous-figure tests made in preliminary analysis of audio amplifier malfunction?
6. State three common errors in component and device replacement.
7. Explain the basic difference between a harmonic-distortion test and an intermodulation-distortion test.
8. State an approximate output-voltage level for a tape deck.
9. Describe a quick and efficient method of checking stereo separation.
10. How can a quick-check be utilized to pinpoint noisy devices or components in an audio amplifier?

Chapter 6

Public Address System Repair

6-1 Basic Survey

Public address sound equipment is basically different from high-fidelity equipment in that PA installations serve a function of speech reinforcement in large open areas or within large enclosed areas. Intelligibility is the central consideration in PA performance, and factors such as percentage distortion and frequency response are seldom measured. Instead, the merit of a PA system is generally evaluated solely on the basis of listening tests. Both indoor and outdoor installations are in wide use (see Figure 6-1). Outdoor systems employ weatherproof folded-horn speakers; indoor or protected systems often utilize sound columns (towers) that typically include six cone-type speakers in each column. Mixers are usually provided: for example, a typical unit accommodates four microphones and an auxiliary/phono signal source. Each mixer input channel has its individual calibrated volume control. In addition, master volume and tone controls enable convenient variation of the total sound-output signal.

From the repairman's viewpoint, the long audio lines that are installed for various PA systems are a potential source of trouble symptoms. Outdoor installations, particularly, often employ exposed lines that may be subject to physical damage. Other outdoor PA installations utilize buried audio cables and are less subject to physical damage. However, such cables are sometimes damaged by trenchers or other construction and maintenance equipment. In addition, buried audio cables occasionally develop cracks or defective joints that admit water. In turn, the conductors may become cor-

(a)

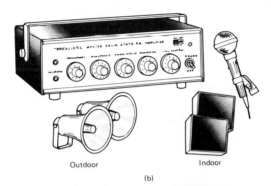

Outdoor   Indoor

(b)

(c)

Fig. 6-1   Basic PA systems. (a) Minimal arrangement; (b) elaborated arrangement with indoor and outdoor speakers; (c) wide coverage system with sound columns. (Courtesy, Radio Shack)

roded and electrical leakage may occur between conductors. When power lines are installed in the vicinity of exposed PA audio lines, an objectionable hum voltage is sometimes introduced into the PA system. Although this remark anticipates subsequent discussion, we can note that hum pickup can be minimized or eliminated by employment of balanced audio lines or by the use of shielded audio cable for single-ended lines. A typical PA audio line installation is depicted in Figure 6-2.

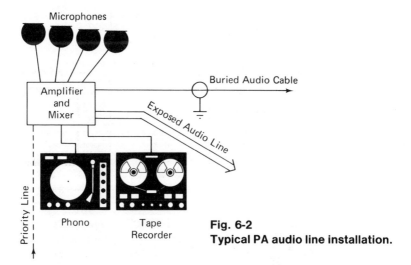

Fig. 6-2
Typical PA audio line installation.

6-2   70.7-Volt and 25-Volt PA Systems

Either a 70.7-volt or a 25-volt "constant-voltage" audio system minimizes impedance-matching problems and permits higher operating efficiency in comparison with low-voltage/low-impedance PA networks. The 70.7-volt system is preferred for high-power PA networks. Figure 6-3 depicts a 70.7-volt matching network for three speakers. A matching transformer is installed to match a speaker or a group of speakers to the 70.7-volt line. It is termed a *constant-voltage* system because the line voltage is comparatively unaffected by switching various speakers on or off. Sample network calculations are as follows:

1.   Determine the power rating of each speaker.
2.   Add the various power values to find the total power demand and use a 70.7-volt amplifier with a power-output rating at least equal to this demand value.
3.   Select a 70.7-volt matching transformer for each speaker (or for each group of speakers) with appropriate primary wattage ratings.

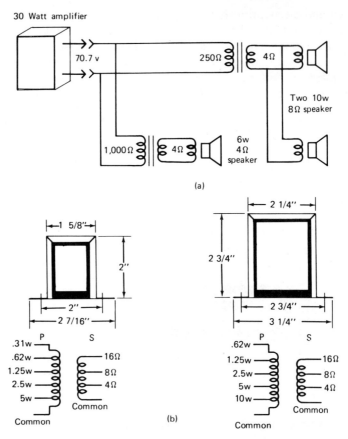

Fig. 6-3   Example of a 70.7-volt speaker-matching network. (a) Configuration; (b) typical 70.7-volt transformer taps and dimensions.

4. Connect the primary terminals of each transformer across the 70.7-volt line from the amplifier output. Note that a primary mismatch up to 25 percent is tolerable.

5. Connect the secondary terminals of each transformer to its speaker (or group of speakers), observing proper connection to the matching ohms tap.

6. In case the matching transformers might be rated in impedance values, the primary wattage of a transformer may be calculated as follows:

$$Z_p = \frac{70.7^2}{P}$$

where Z_p is the rated primary impedance and P is the wattage rating of the speaker.

It follows that the following power and impedance relations result:

$$1 \text{ watt corresponds to } 5,000 \text{ ohms } Z_p$$
$$2 \text{ watts correspond to } 2,500 \text{ ohms } Z_p$$
$$5 \text{ watts correspond to } 1,000 \text{ ohms } Z_p$$
$$10 \text{ watts correspond to } 500 \text{ ohms } Z_p$$

In the more elaborate designs of PA systems, a priority paging switch is provided for one of the microphone inputs. This priority switch permits the operator to "break in" for special announcements. An output jack may also be included for tape-recording the audio signal. A comparatively versatile PA amplifier is illustrated in Figure 6-4.

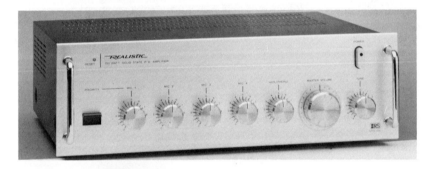

(a)

Fig. 6-4 A versatile 100-watt PA amplifier and typical outdoor speaker. (a) View of control panel; (b) weatherproof folded horn. (Courtesy, Radio Shack)

(b)

6-3 PA Acoustic Environments

The audio repairman is often required to evaluate and report upon existing, proposed, or extended PA acoustic environments. For instance, a PA system in a convention hall operates in an enclosed space, and the environment may be very noisy at times. On the other hand, a PA system at an athletic event operates in a virtually open area in which the noise level may be high or low. A PA system in a factory often operates in a very noisy aural environment. Conversely, a PA system in a hotel lobby usually operates in a quiet environment. Acoustic factors in some PA systems can be troublesome—thus, a PA system in a large railway depot or a large airport lobby with many corridors must contend with a highly reverberant acoustic environment that develops lingering echoes. When trains or planes are arriving or departing, a very high noise-level factor must also be contended with. In this situation, it is advantageous to install numerous small speakers spaced at comparatively close intervals. When the noise level is unusually high, it is advantageous to provide a high-level switch for the operator, whereby more audio power may be applied to the speakers when needed. A standard noise-level chart is shown in Table 6-1, and a speaker input power chart is shown in Table 6-2.

Table 6-1   Sound Level Chart

General Location Description	Noise Level In dB	Noise Quality
Factory (Very Noisy)		Very Noisy—
Machine Shop (Average)	90	Conversation
Printing Plant	80	Difficult or Impossible
Ball Room (Normal Use)		Noisy—
Restaurant (Noisy)		Voice Must
Assembly Line (Noisy)	75	Be Raised
Factory (Average)		To Be
Machine Accounting Area	70	Understood
R.R. or Bus Depot		
Auditorium (Average)		
Shipping/Receiving Dept.		
Department Store		Normal—
Auditorium (Quiet)	65	Normal
Restaurant (Average)		Conversation
Store (Quiet)	60	Easily
Office (Quiet)		Understood
Hotel Lobby	55	
Doctors Waiting Room		

—Courtesy, Allied Electronics

Table 6-2 Speaker Input Power Chart

The chart below has been designed to help you determine your speaker and amplification requirements in relation to the environmental noise level

Total Number of Speakers	Total Amplification Recommended (in watts)		
	Normal	Noisy	Very Noisy
1	½	2	5
2	1	4	10
3	1½	6	15
4	2	8	20
5	2½	10	25
10	5	20	50
20	10	40	100
50	25	100	250
100	50	200	500
150	75	300	750
200	100	400	1000
500	250	1000	2500
750	375	1500	3750
1000	500	2000	5000

—Courtesy, Allied Electronics

6-4 Principles of Speech Reinforcement

Since the human voice has a comparatively low energy level, it can ordinarily cover only a limited area, even in a good PA acoustic environment. Accordingly, speech-reinforcement arrangements are in wide use. Few of these installations qualify as high-fidelity sound systems, and some of them reproduce very mediocre sound. However, utility is the basic consideration, and the chief criterion of a speech-reinforcement system is its information-transfer capability (intelligibility). If spoken words can be properly understood, even mediocre reproduction at a distance of a hundred feet from the source is highly utilitarian and serves a most useful purpose. A wide frequency range is not required for acceptable articulation in a speech-reinforcement system, as indicated in Figure 6-5. It is generally considered that a frequency range from 200 Hz to 2 kHz is adequate for satisfactory articulation. However, there is an unavoidable "side effect" in that this limited frequency range impairs the "naturalness" of the speaker's voice to some extent.

Thus, a speech-reinforcement system is primarily regarded as a means of information transfer—not as a mode of entertainment. With reference to

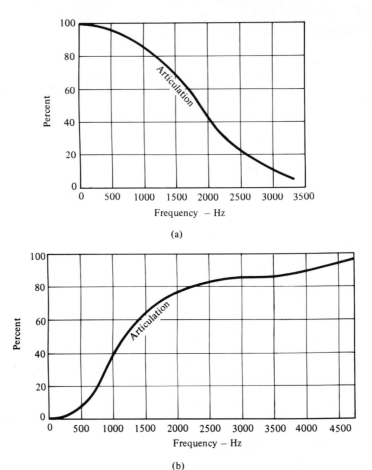

(a)

(b)

Fig. 6-5   **Effect of frequency response on articulation. (a) Percent articulation when low frequencies to left of curve are cut off; (b) percent articulation when high frequencies to right of curve are cut off.**

Figure 6-6, it is evident that two sound sources must be taken into consideration in a speech-reinforcement system. A listener positioned halfway between a lectern and a speech-reinforcement speaker will hear essentially the same sound from the lectern and from the speaker. In other words, part of the perceived sound energy arrives from the orator, and another part of the sound energy arrives from the speech-reinforcement speaker. Since both of these sound wavefronts are perceived simultaneously by the listener, there is no delay distortion involved, which could impair articulation. Effectively, only the total sound level at the listening position is increased. Of course, this basic discussion will be subject to modification in the event that the prevailing acoustic environment is not suitable for reproduction of a second sound source to the rear of the listening position.

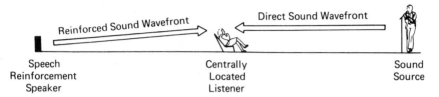

Fig. 6-6   **Centrally located listener perceives a higher total sound level than from front or rear alone.**

Next, consider a listener seated toward the rear of a highly reverberant hall, as depicted in Figure 6-7. Substantial reflection of sound occurs from the far end of the hall, although no speech reinforcement equipment is utilized. The listener experiences an increased sound level owing to the reverberant energy. On the other hand, the reverberant energy arrives with an excessive time delay that results in an area of confusion with poor articulation. With reference to Figure 6-7(b), another situation with a sound-reinforcement arrangement that results in an area of confusion is shown; unequal time delays result in poor articulation. That is, the listener is seated near the rear of a long hall that has acceptable acoustic characteristics and which is provided with a speech-reinforcement speaker at the rear—but the listener is in an area of confusion owing to the disparity in arrival times between the sound-reinforcement wavefront and the direct sound wavefront. This problem can be overcome by employment of a time-delay unit in the audio line, as shown in Figure 6-7(c). This time-delay unit equalizes the time of arrival for the sound-reinforcement wavefront and the direct sound wavefront at the listening position.

6-5   Audio Time Delay Basics

Excessive disparity in arrival times of two sound wavefronts carrying the same audio information results in poor intelligibility. From a practical point of view, the maximum tolerable delay time between direct and reinforcement wavefronts is 25 milliseconds, approximately. This basic value varies to some extent depending upon the relative intensities of the two sound wavefronts. A time delay (echo time) greater than the critical value results in a confusing "separation effect" that impairs intelligibility. The listener's direction-perception or position-perception process then jumps from one source to the other, thereby producing a reaction of distraction or annoyance. In addition, syllabic overlap impairs articulation at the listening position. Inasmuch as the human ear has a natural tolerance for everyday

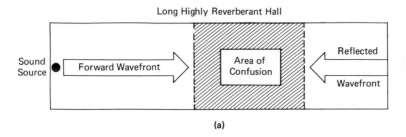

Long Highly Reverberant Hall

(a)

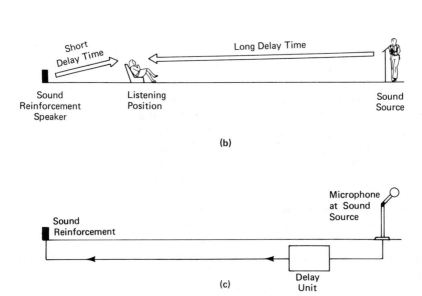

(b)

(c)

Fig. 6-7 **Excessive time delay reduces articulation and confuses the listener. (a) Long, highly reverberant hall; (b) rear sound reinforcement speaker improves articulation; (c) delay unit in audio line improves articulation at rear of hall.**

echo effects, the listener tends to disregard an ordinary echo, even in a mediocre acoustic environment. On the other hand, if an echo is excessively delayed, the listener is no longer able to blend and unify the two wavefronts, and he experiences a feeling of confusion. In turn, he reacts with annoyance to the split-sound sources (see Figure 6-8).

The critical value in wavefront arrival times depends to some extent upon the relative sound intensities of the two wavefronts. Under ordinary conditions, an echo is weaker than the direct wavefront from the sound

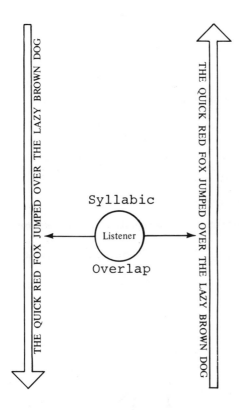

Fig. 6-8
Visualization of split-sound source perception.

source. In turn, it is understandable that the human ear has less tolerance for echoes that have greater intensities than the direct wavefront arriving from the source. As an illustration, in a sound-reinforcement system, 10 percent of the listeners will be disturbed if the PA sound level is 3 dB below the source level and is delayed 60 milliseconds. Again, 10 percent of the listeners will be disturbed if the PA sound level is 6 dB below the source level and is delayed 80 milliseconds. On the other hand, 10 percent of the listeners will be disturbed if the PA sound level is 10 dB above the source level and is delayed 30 milliseconds. Accordingly, no listener within range of the PA sound field should be exposed to two sound wavefronts that are separated by more than 25 milliseconds in time. This requirement is summarized in the Haas-effect diagram shown in Figure 6-9.

With reference to Figure 6-10, it is seen that the relationship of echo delay time to echo intensity is approximately in direct proportion for those echoes that are weaker than the direct sound wavefront. However, this relationship increases out of proportion with great rapidity as the echo intensity begins to exceed the intensity of the direct sound wavefront. Thus, if the guideline of less than 10 percent listener disturbance is observed, a delay

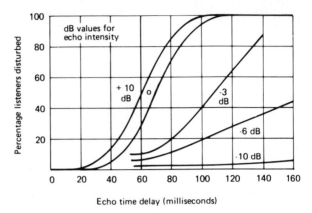

Fig. 6-9   Time-delay disturbance versus intensity of a reflected sound.

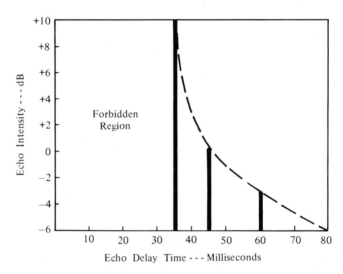

Fig. 6-10   Maximum permissible echo delay time versus echo intensity for less than 10 percent listener disturbance.

time of 35 milliseconds and an echo intensity of +10 dB represent the absolute maxima for a sound-reinforcement system. Conservative planning would regard a delay time of 25 milliseconds and an echo intensity of +6 dB as suitable design limits. Note that the comparative intensities of a direct wavefront and a sound-reinforcement wavefront can be measured with a sound-level meter by first switching out of the direct speaker(s), and then by switching in direct speaker(s) and switching out the sound-reinforcement speaker(s).

6-6 Delay Compensation

A cluster of speakers, as exemplified in Figure 6-11, or a speaker column (tower) can provide considerable acoustic coverage. Nevertheless, difficulties may be encountered in large listening areas with substantial reverberation. In such problem situations, the PA system can be improved by supplementing a large speaker cluster or column with smaller columns located at progressive intervals back from the primary sound source. In turn, the primary sound source can be operated at a lower output level; that is, its reduced output is progressively reinforced by the smaller speaker installations. Thereby all of the listeners in the area will experience an increased proportion of direct sound and a lesser proportion of reverberant sound. For instance, a large speaker cluster or column installed near the rostrum may cover a distance up to 100 feet. Beyond this point, additional coverage may be provided by a supplementary speaker column, as shown in Figure 6-12.

Fig. 6-11   A speaker cluster for an open air PA system.

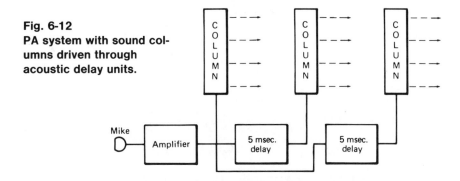

**Fig. 6-12
PA system with sound columns driven through acoustic delay units.**

Note that past a distance of 100 feet, an acoustic delay device is then needed to process the audio signal and to delay the arrival of the sound wavefront from the first column by 5 milliseconds before the sound from the second column is radiated. Next, at the following 50-foot interval, a second supplementary column should be installed with a time-delay device whereby its localized listeners will perceive a sound wavefront from the main column first, followed 5 milliseconds later by the wavefront from the first supplementary column, and then followed after another 5-millisecond delay by the sound wavefront from the second supplementary column. Observe also that the intensity of the delayed sound should not be more than 10 dB greater than that of the wavefront that first arrives. Otherwise, the listener is likely to experience a split-sound effect ("acoustic separation") of the two sources.

Time-delay units for PA systems commonly utilize a tape recorder with suitably spaced recording and playback heads, as shown in principle in Figure 6-13. Some systems employ magnetic-disk record/playback units. The most recent designs use "bucket-brigade" large-scale integrated (LSI) devices for time delay. With reference to Figure 6-12, it is essential to limit the proportion of sound energy that is radiated from a speaker toward the front of the building or the listening area. That is, rearward radiation from a delayed sound source should be at least 6 dB less than the forward radiation from the souce. This reduction in rearward radiation can be assisted by means of the acoustic treatment portrayed in Figure 6-14. A layer of cotton or fiberglass 2 inches thick is cemented to the rear surface of the speaker column. This layer not only tends to absorb incident sound energy that is incident or diffused to the layer, but also serves to change the phase of any sound energy radiated from the back of the column by an amount equal to

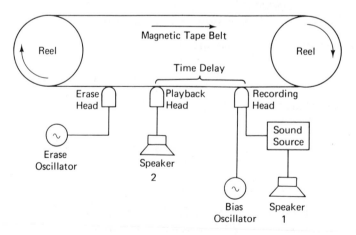

Fig. 6-13   Principles of a magnetic-tape delay unit.

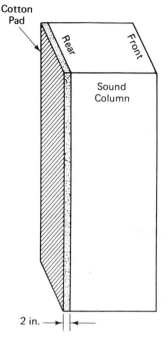

Cotton
Pad

Rear

Front

Sound
Column

2 in.

Fig. 6-14 **Cotton pad reduces rearward acoustic radiation from sound column.**

the phase change entailed by the sound waves in traveling from the front of the column around to its rear surface. These acoustic reactions serve to reduce substantially the intensity of rearward-radiated sound. In particularly difficult situations, the problem of rearward radiation can be further reduced by restricting the frequency range of the PA system as required, provided that intelligibility is not objectionably impaired.

6-7 Positive Feedback and Equalization

If the positive acoustic feedback energy from speaker(s) to microphone exceeds a critical value, the PA system will "howl" at the frequency of maximum feedback. This principle is depicted in Figures 6-15 and 6-16. Practical methods are available to control excessive positive feedback. First, the troubleshooter should experiment with various orientations of highly directive microphones. One of the most directional types of microphone is the "short gun" design pictured in Figure 6-16(c). This form of microphone is highly directional at frequencies above 500 Hz and has a cardioid acceptance pattern for frequencies below 500 Hz. In particularly difficult situations, the troubleshooter may need to use a frequency trap, as shown in Figure 6-17. This is basically a notch filter. Its rejection frequency and bandwidth are dependent upon R and C values; to "trim" the filter response, the troubleshooter should vary the R and C values as required with the aid of resistor and capacitor decade boxes.

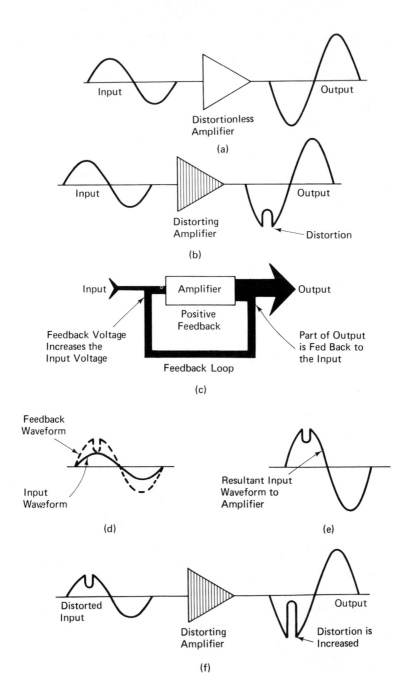

Fig. 6-15 **Positive feedback increases distortion. (a) Amplifier with distortionless output; (b) amplifier with distorted output; (c) amplifier with positive-feedback loop; (d) input and feedback waveforms are in phase; (e) resultant input waveform to amplifier; (f) output waveform is further distorted by the amplifier.**

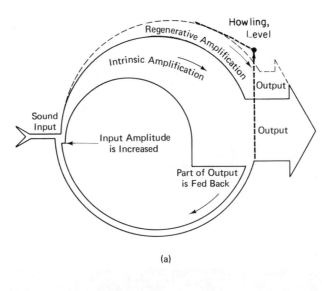

(a)

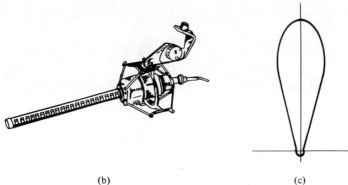

(b)   (c)

Fig. 6-16   **Principle of positive feedback. (a) Feedback energy adds to input; (b) "short gun" type of microphone; (c) acceptance pattern.**

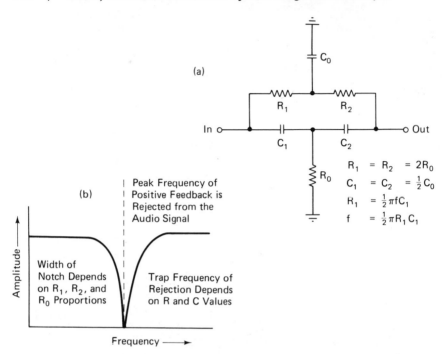

(a)

$R_1 = R_2 = 2R_0$

$C_1 = C_2 = \frac{1}{2}C_0$

$R_1 = \frac{1}{2}\pi f C_1$

$f = \frac{1}{2}\pi R_1 C_1$

(b)

Peak Frequency of Positive Feedback is Rejected from the Audio Signal

Width of Notch Depends on R_1, R_2, and R_0 Proportions

Trap Frequency of Rejection Depends on R and C Values

(c)

Fig. 6-17   **A parallel-T frequency-rejection trap. (a) Configuration; (b) filter frequency characteristics; (c) frequency responses provided by a parametric equalizer.**

In some situations, a parametric equalizer may serve the purpose, instead of a specialized notch filter. A parametric equalizer has adjustable responses, as exemplified in Figure 6-17(c). Controls are provided for adjustment of center frequency, filter bandwidth (Q value), and amplitude of the boost or cut frequency characteristic. A parametric equalizer includes operational amplifiers (op amps) to provide precise control of filter characteristics and also to overcome the insertion loss that would be imposed by passive circuitry.

6-8   Audio Signal Mixing

In case that a PA amplifier does not include audio mixing facilities, or if an insufficient number of channels are provided, the technician may utilize a separate mixer unit, as shown in Figure 6-18. This unit provides four additional variable-level input channels with extensive isolation between channels. The single output terminal is connected to the input terminal of the PA preamplifier or to one of the input channels of an amplifier that has multiple inputs. Emitter-follower output is utilized in the mixer circuit design to make the output circuit practically immune to disturbance by load-impedance changes. The field-effect transistor indicated has a rated gain of 17 dB, so that a wide range of input signal levels can be effectively mixed and balanced. Although the bipolar resistor develops no voltage gain, it provides substantial current gain and power gain.

6-9   Balanced and Unbalanced Lines

With reference to Figure 6-19, a PA system may utilize either balanced or unbalanced lines. A balanced line is particularly advantageous when an open-line run picks up excessive hum voltage. To change from an unbalanced input or unbalanced run to a balanced arrangement, the differential-amplifier configuration shown in Figure 6-19(d) can be used, with one of its input terminals grounded. Thus a single-ended input terminal is converted into a pair of double-ended output terminals. A balanced line rejects hum voltage that may be picked up from stray fields because the induced voltage has the same polarity in both of the line wires. On the other hand, the audio signal voltage has opposite polarities in the two line wires. Consequently, the hum voltage cancels out in the balanced load whereas the audio voltages do not cancel out.

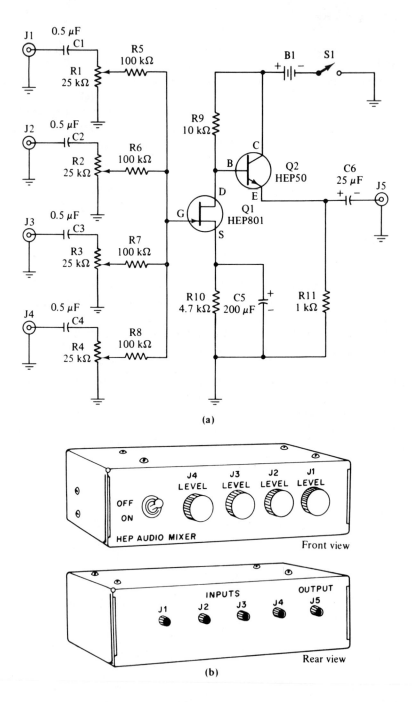

(a)

(b)

Fig. 6-18 Audio mixer. (a) Configuration; (b) appearance. (Courtesy, Motorola)

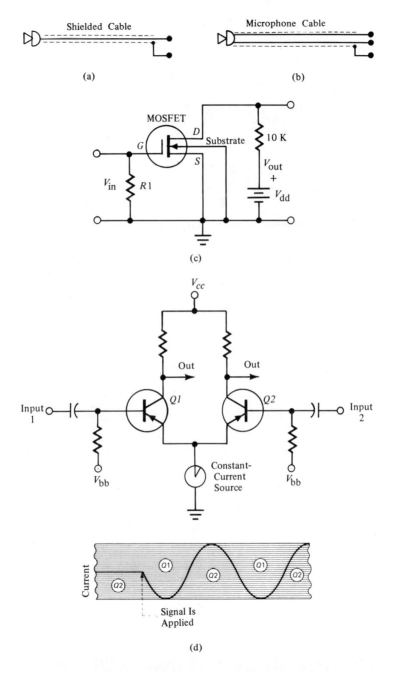

Fig. 6-19 Microphone input circuits. (a) Unbalanced microphone line; (b) balanced microphone line; (c) unbalanced recorder input circuit; (d) balanced recorder input circuit; (e) a 10-kHz push-pull signal with 60-Hz common-mode interference; (f) differential input rejects the 60-Hz interference. (Figure continued)

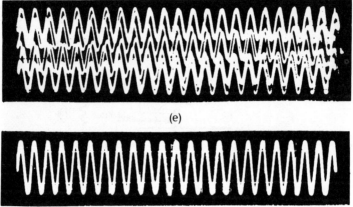

(e)

(f)

Fig. 6-19   Continued.

Review Questions

1. What is the basic distinction between a PA installation and a hi-fi system?
2. Explain briefly how a 70.7-V PA system functions.
3. Give an example of a difficult acoustic environment.
4. Why does excessive delay time between direct sound wavefronts and reinforced sound wavefronts reduce articulation?
5. Describe a typical speaker cluster.
6. How does a magnetic-tape audio delay unit function?
7. Define positive feedback and explain how it can be controlled.
8. What is an audio mixer?
9. Why are balanced microphone lines often used instead of single-ended microphone lines?
10. Briefly describe the differential-amplifier arrangement.

Chapter 7

Radio Receiver and Transceiver Repair

7-1 General Principles

Three basic types of radio equipment are encountered by the electronic repairman: receivers, transmitters, and transceivers. Subclasses of radio equipment include radio control units, wireless alarm systems, radio direction finders, and wireless microphones. Radio receivers are fundamentally classified into amplitude-modulation (AM) and frequency-modulation (FM) types. Telemetry radio systems employ various forms of pulse-code modulation (PCM). Radio receivers are further subdivided into broadcast-frequency, high-frequency, and low-frequency designs. High-frequency radio receivers, transmitters, and transceivers are also classified into double-sideband, single-sideband-with-carrier, and single-sideband varieties. The most basic radio tests and measurements can be categorized as follows: signal-tracing, signal-substitution, alignment checks, distortion tests, sensitivity measurements, modulation checks, power-output measurements, signal/noise ratio measurements, and capture-ratio tests (see Figure 7-1).

Signal-tracing tests are made to best advantage with an oscilloscope. An oscilloscope used in general radio diagnostic procedures should have extended high-frequency response, such as 15 MHz or 30 MHz. For instance, the citizens-band (CB) channel-frequency allocations are approximately in the 27-MHz region, as listed in Table 7-1. Accordingly, an oscilloscope with 30-MHz vertical-amplifier response can be used to check the percentage modulation and linearity of modulation in a CB transmitter circuit directly, whereas an oscilloscope with 15-MHz response must be applied indirectly in

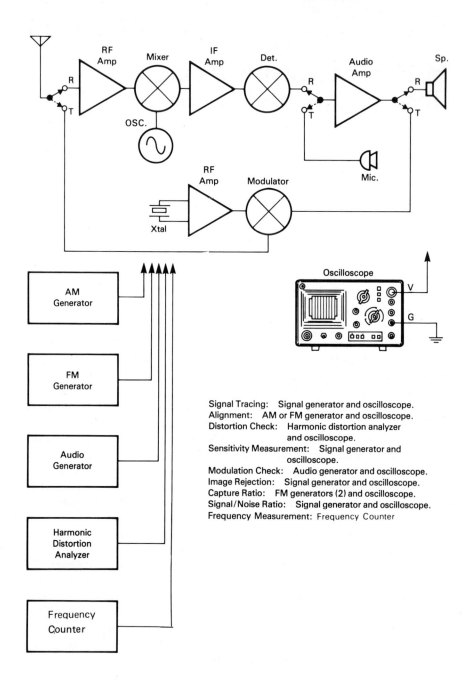

Fig. 7-1   Nine basic radio diagnostic tests.

Table 7-1 CB Channel Frequency Allocations

Channel	Frequency, MHz	Channel	Frequency, MHz
1	26.965	21	27.215
2	26.975	22	27.225
3	26.985	23	27.235
4	27.005	24	27.245
5	27.015	25	27.255
6	27.025	26	27.265
7	27.035	27	27.275
8	27.055	28	27.285
9	27.065	29	27.295
10	27.075	30	27.305
11	27.085	31	27.315
12	27.105	32	27.325
13	27.115	33	27.335
14	27.125	34	27.345
15	27.135	35	27.355
16	27.155	36	27.365
17	27.165	37	27.375
18	27.175	38	27.385
19	27.185	39	27.395
20	27.205	40	27.405

combination with supplementary equipment. Although an oscilloscope used in radio diagnostic procedures is more versatile if it has high sensitivity, a tradeoff is involved in that an oscilloscope that has extended high-frequency response generally has comparatively low sensitivity. Therefore, many radio repairmen keep two oscilloscopes at hand, one of which has extended high-frequency response with moderate sensitivity, the other with moderate high-frequency response (such as 2 MHz or 3 MHz) and high sensitivity.

7-2 Signal Substitution

Signal-substitution tests are made to best advantage with AM and FM signal generators. Various kinds of AM generators are employed in radio diagnostic procedures. They are basically divided into service-type and lab-type generators. The distinction between them is that a service-type generator has moderate accuracy, uncalibrated output, and a signal waveform that contains harmonics as exemplified in Figure 7-2. On the other hand, a lab-type generator has high accuracy, an output meter with a calibrated attenuator, and a sinusoidal signal waveform with a very low harmonic content. Service-type signal generators are adequate for signal-subsitution and other qualitative tests. A lab-type AM generator must be used for precise quantitative tests and measurements. A frequency-modulation (FM) generator should have a uniform (flat) output over the swept band; if it does not contain built-in marker facilities, it should be supplemented by a crystal-oscillator source of key frequencies or by a highly accurate lab-type AM generator.

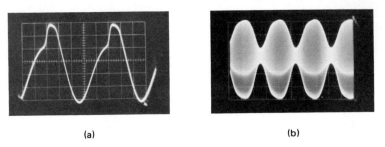

(a)   (b)

Fig. 7-2   **Typical output signal waveforms from a service-type AM signal generator. (a) RF waveform; (b) modulated RF waveform.**

7-3 Radio Receiver Features

Basic classifications of AM radio receivers are noted in Figure 7-3. Different categories of receivers have essential technical differences in circuit action, which are of central concern in diagnostic procedures. If the repairman does not take these technical distinctions into account, he will be handicapped in eradicating trouble conditions and will be unable to make definitive tests. The four general categories of AM receivers include the superheterodyne, superregenerative, regenerative, and direct-conversion types. Superheterodyne designs are subdivided into single-conversion, dual-conversion, and triple-conversion types. The majority of AM receivers employ single conversion; broadcast/short-wave and public-service receivers often utilize double conversion; wide-range receivers that cover from 10 kHz to 30MHz, for example, generally use triple conversion. Superheterodyne receivers are also characterized as double-sideband, single-sideband, or single-sideband/suppressed-carrier varieties. Communications receivers employ the greatest degree of design sophistication, and they make the maximum demands on a repairman's knowledge and expertise. Communication-type receivers are subclassified as follows:

1. Receivers of professional design for communications and data transmissions including code or voice information, with maximum performance in each area of application. The entire high-frequency range is generally covered.

2. Receivers of relaxed professional design for application in the communications are less sensitive and may have fewer operating features; they generally cover the entire high-frequency range.

3. General-purpose communications receivers are comparatively less elaborate and have reduced performance capability. Some designs cover the entire high-frequency range, whereas others cover only specialized ranges or only the amateur bands.

4. Communications receivers of the economy type are designed with considerably relaxed electrical and mechanical specifications. Most receivers in this category are limited to specialized frequency ranges or to amateur bands only.

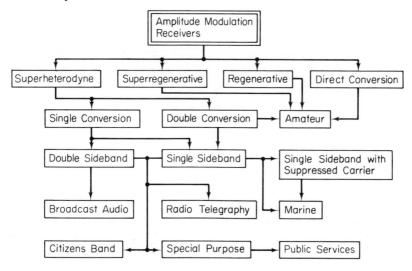

Fig. 7-3   Basic classifications of AM radio receivers.

Diagnostic procedures require recognition of four types of oscillator injection modes. These modes determine the frequency relations with which the repairman is concerned. With reference to Figure 7-4, a single injection frequency is utilized in a conventional single-conversion superheterodyne. This arrangement is used, for example, in virtually all AM and FM broadcast receivers. Single conversion is also utilized in a large proportion of special-purpose receivers (but only in a minority of CB receivers). Note that standard 40-channel CB transceivers include phase-locked loops (PLL's) to generate the receive and transmit injection frequencies with a minimum complement of oscillator crystals. Both digital and analog circuitry are utilized in phase-locked loops. With reference to Figure 7-5, a heterodyne synthesizer is depicted in skeleton form for a 23-channel CB receiver, wherein only 14 oscillator crystals are required to generate the 46 channel frequencies that are required.

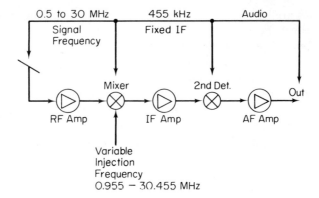

Fig. 7-4 **Functional block diagram of a conventional single-conversion superheterodyne receiver.**

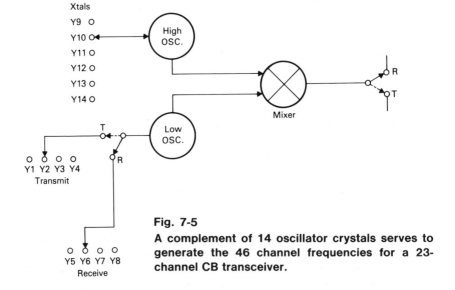

Fig. 7-5

A complement of 14 oscillator crystals serves to generate the 46 channel frequencies for a 23-channel CB transceiver.

7-4 Double Conversion

Confusion in diagnostic procedures is virtually certain to occur in double-conversion superheterodyne circuitry (Figure 7-6), unless the troubleshooter recognizes the two injection-frequency sections. In this example, a variable-oscillator (VFO) injection frequency is followed by a fixed-oscillator injection frequency. This elaboration of the basic superheterodyne arrangement is employed in various two-way receivers, in CB receivers, and in the more sophisticated types of communications receivers. In the case of a CB receiver, the first injection frequency is adjustable in steps (not continuously variable); the injection frequency is changed in discrete steps by means of a switch control. If a heterodyne frequency synthesizer is utilized, the adjustable injection frequency is generated as shown in Figure 7-7. To generate injection frequencies separated by 10-kHz steps, the phase comparator operates with a 10-kHz frequency at both inputs. A frequency divider changes the standard frequency to 10 kHz. The programmable frequency divider is controlled by switching circuits. Note that the output from the voltage-controlled oscillator (VCO) is in 10-kHz steps, but the least significant figure for each channel frequency is 5 kHz. Accordingly, another crystal oscillator is included to provide for the 5-kHz factor.

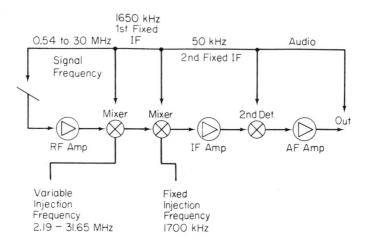

Fig. 7-6   **Functional block diagram of a double-conversion super-heterodyne.**

7-5   Principal Circuit Sections

In the first analysis, a complete radio receiver may be regarded as a signal-processing system that comprises four principal circuit sections, as depicted in Figure 7-8. These sections are:

1. Signal path circuits
2. Frequency-determining circuits

3. Control circuits
4. Power circuits

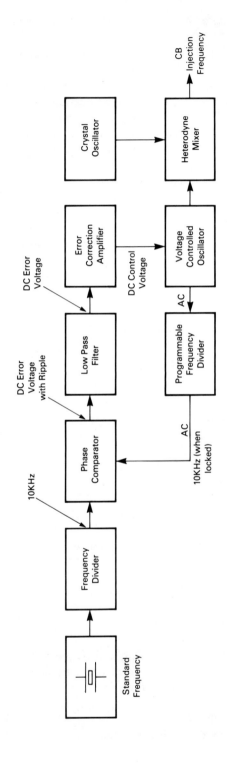

Fig. 7-7   Example of a heterodyne frequency synthesizer with phase-locked loop for CB reception.

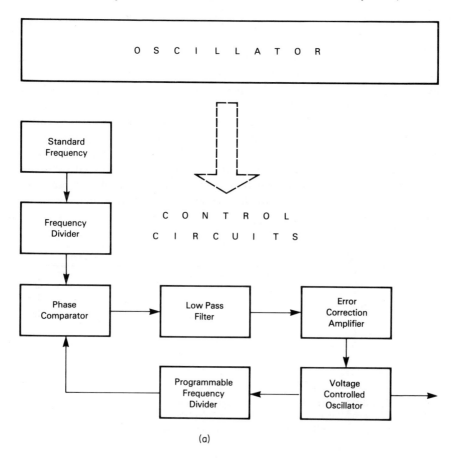

(a)

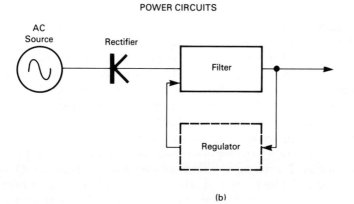

(b)

Fig. 7-8   Basic sections of radio receivers.

With reference to Figure 7-9, a typical variable first-IF receiver arrangement is shown. Note that the circuit after the first mixer comprises a conventional first-IF network that tunes from 1.5 MHz to 2.5 MHz. The first mixer translates all incoming frequencies to the 1.5-MHz to 2.5-MHz range by mixing them with a series of stepped injection frequencies spaced 1 MHz apart. To receive the 4.5-MHz to 5.5-MHz band, for example, a 7-MHz frequency is injected into the first mixer. A 5.5-MHz incoming signal beating with the 7-MHz injection frequency produces a difference frequency of 1.5 MHz, which falls within the range of the variable first-IF section. The injection frequencies for the first mixer can be provided by a crystal oscillator (translation oscillator) with switchable crystals spaced 1 MHz apart. The variable injection frequencies for the second mixer are provided by an interpolation oscillator.

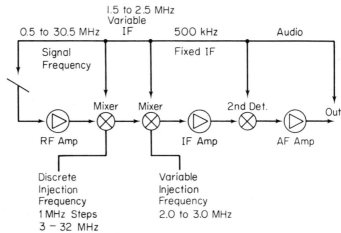

Fig. 7-9   **A dual-superheterodyne arrangement with a variable first-IF section.**

Injection frequencies are provided by various kinds of oscillators. Graphical symbols for typical frequency-determining circuits are shown in Figure 7-10. Note that a continuously variable injection frequency may be developed from a switched (adjustable) high-frequency oscillator. Limited-range variable-frequency oscillators may be either capacitively or inductively tuned. Only a single frequency is required for injection to the mixer of a double-conversion, fixed first-IF superheterodyne, and this single frequency may be supplied by a crystal oscillator. Discrete stepped frequencies for the first mixer of a variable first-IF receiver may also be supplied by a crystal oscillator. Premixing is a form of frequency synthesis in which the final frequencies applied to the signal mixer are synthesized from other frequencies in a series of circuits, as shown in Figure 7-11 (see also Figure 7-12).

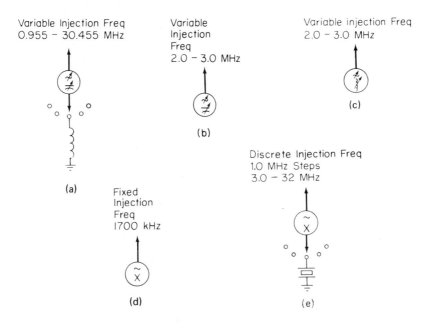

Fig. 7-10   **Graphical symbols for various frequency-determining circuits.**

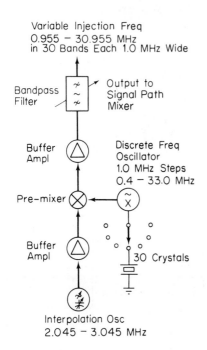

Fig. 7-11
Premixer (partial) synthesis enables a single-conversion superheterodyne to be precisely calibrated.

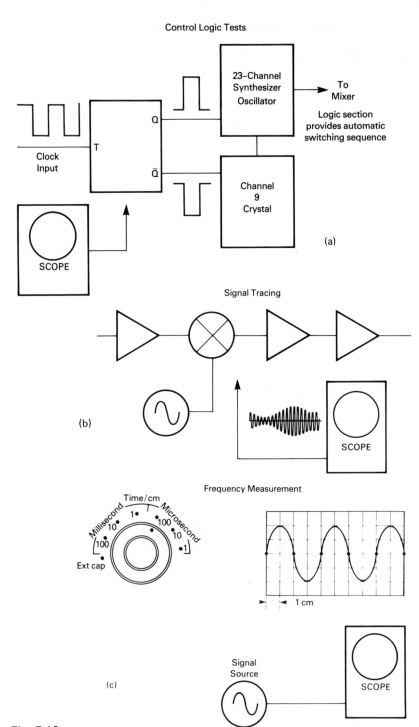

Fig. 7-12
Basic tests in radio receiver circuitry.

Alignment Check

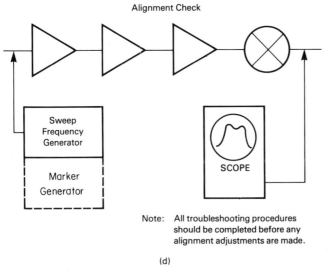

Note: All troubleshooting procedures should be completed before any alignment adjustments are made.

(d)

Gain Measurement

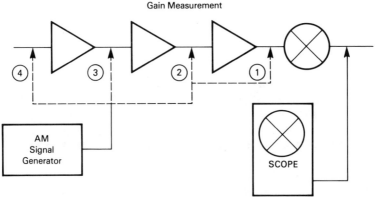

Fig. 7-12   Continued.   (e)

7-6 Frequency Synthesizer

A simplified functional block diagram of a frequency synthesizer used in an elaborate communications receiver is shown in Figure 7-13. A phase-locked oscillator is employed to generate the actual frequency that is injected into the first mixer. This phase-locked oscillator provides any one of 59 discrete frequencies spaced 500 kHz apart from 46.625 MHz to 71.625 MHz. The oscillator is controlled and locked in at 500-kHz intervals by a series of control frequencies derived from the 1000-kHz reference oscillator, much as the local oscillator in an FM receiver is locked to the signal by auto-

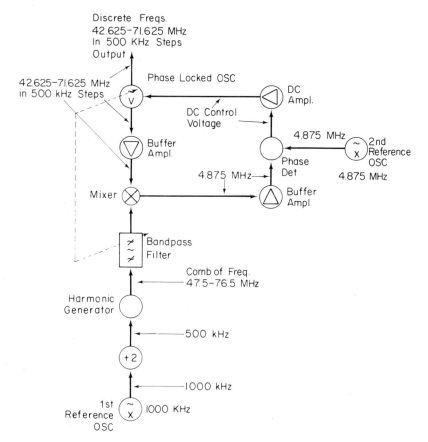

Fig. 7-13 **A frequency synthesizer that covers 500 kHz to 300 MHz in 500-kHz bands.**

matic frequency control (AFC) action. The output from the crystal-controlled 1000-kHz reference oscillator passes through a divide-by-two circuit to produce a 500-kHz frequency, which is applied in turn to a harmonic generator, which in turn generates an array or comb of frequencies.

A chosen frequency from the comb is selected by the filter following the harmonic generator. The frequency selected by the filter is used as the reference to which the phase-locked oscillator (PLO) is synchronized; this selected frequency is always 4.875 MHz higher than the desired output from the PLO. Next, the selected reference frequency is combined with the output from the PLO in the mixer. Their difference frequency is applied to a phase detector. This phase detector generates a control voltage that pulls the phase-locked oscillator on-frequency. In summary, an array of 59 crystal-controlled injection frequencies is generated with only two quartz crystals. Observe that no switching is employed in this type of frequency synthesizer.

7-7   CB Radio Diagnosis and Troubleshooting

It is helpful to consider the fundamentals of CB radio trouble diagnosis. As noted previously, virtually all CB units are transceivers and operate in the 27-MHz band. Note the schematic diagram for a typical three-channel CB transceiver shown in Figure 7-14. Common trouble symptoms are as follows:

No reception: When a no-reception trouble symptom is encountered, check each channel. Turn up the volume control and turn the squelch control to minimum. Noise output will be heard in normal operation, even if there is no incoming signal. If there is no noise output, it may be concluded that the associated channel is dead.

All channels dead: If there is no noise output on any channel, it is likely that the entire transceiver is dead. However, check out the transmitting function while watching the modulation indicator. If the transmitter is functional, the indicator bulb will vary in brightness while the microphone is being spoken into.

Receiver dead, transmitter functional: When there is no noise output on any channel although the transmitter operates normally, the trouble will be found in the receiver section between the antenna and the detector. For example, with reference to Figure 7-14, D1 or D2 might be found short-circuited or open-circuited.

Noise output on all channels but one: When there is noise output on all channels but one, there is likely to be a defective quartz crystal in the associated channel circuitry, or possibly a defect in the channel-selector switch.

Noise output on one channel only: If there is noise output on one channel only, check the channel-selector switch.

Squelch control does not work: This trouble symptom directs suspicion to the automatic volume control (AVC) voltage. An incorrect value of AVC voltage is likely to be caused by a leaky capacitor in the AVC section; check also the capacitors in the squelch section.

Weak reception: If reception is weak and the antenna has been checked, the defective stage can be localized by means of signal-tracing or signal-substitution tests. The faulty component or device can generally be pinpointed by DC voltage and resistance measurements.

Receiver overloads on strong signals: When the receiver overloads and distorts on strong signals and provides normal reception on weak signals, the AVC voltage is likely to be off-value. A leaky capacitor is the most probable cause.

Intermittent reception: Some intermittents are mechanical, some are thermal, and others are activated by transient voltages. Check to determine whether the volume control or the squelch control may have become erratic. Also check the channel-selector switch for defective contacts. Sometimes intermittents are caused by defective insulation on leads. Another common cause is loose pressure contacts or cold-soldered joints. It is helpful to monitor the signal voltage with an oscilloscope and to monitor the DC voltage at the collector of a suspected transistor and note any changes upon occurrence of the intermittent condition. Capacitors may become intermittent; occasionally, a resistor, diode, or transistor will become intermittent. Quartz crystals sometimes develop marginal defects.

Subnormal RF power output: When the collector DC power input to the final amplifier is 5 watts, the RF power output is typically 3 watts. An RF wattmeter is generally used to measure the RF power output (see Figure 7-

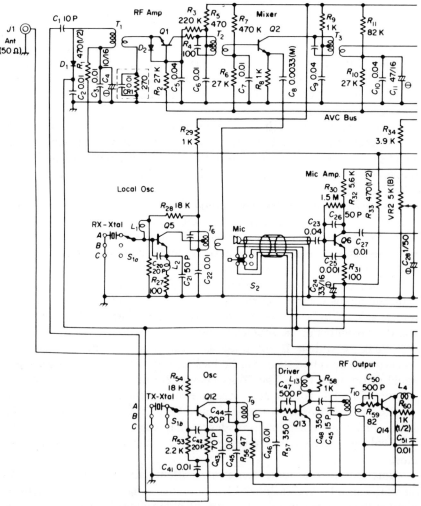

Fig. 7-14 Schematic diagram for a three-channel citizens-band transceiver.

15). If the power output is subnormal, a systematic checkout of the transmitter section is necessary. Power-type transistors are likely suspects, followed by capacitors, which may become leaky or open. Note that an RF power transistor may be damaged by loss of normal antenna loading, or by operation without a 50-ohm power resistor to simulate an antenna load.

Off-frequency transmission: Off-frequency transmission is most likely to be caused by a defective transmitter quartz crystal. This trouble symptom may be accompanied by subnormal RF power output. An intermittent trouble symptom is occasionally caused by a marginally defective crystal that jumps frequency after operating normally for a longer or shorter period.

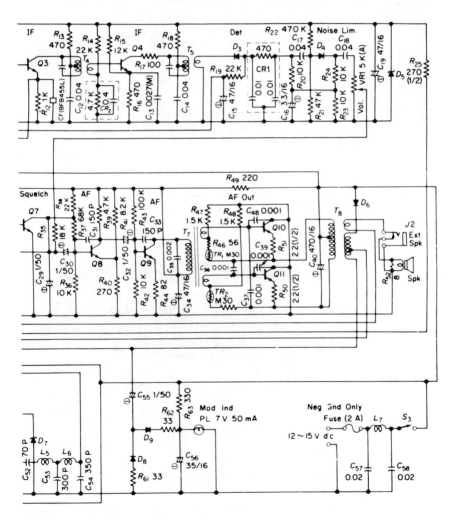

Fig. 7-14   Continued.

Fig. 7-15   A CB analyzer and performance checker includes an RF watt-meter. (Courtesy, Sencore)

Fig. 7-16   A high-performance digital frequency counter. (Courtesy, Sencore)

Before replacing a crystal, however, the oscillator adjustments should be checked. (See T1 in Figure 7-14.) A digital frequency counter (Figure 7-16) may be utilized for precise measurement of the crystal frequency.

RF power output with crystal removed: When off-frequency operation occurs and RF power output continues although the quartz crystal has been unplugged from the transmitter, it is likely that the oscillator, driver, or RF power amplifier stage is self-oscillatory. In many cases, the malfunction is due to an open decoupling or bypass capacitor in the transmitter section.

Modulation trouble symptoms: If there is weak or no modulation of the RF carrier or if there is ample modulation with objectionably distorted output, it is indicated that there is a malfunction in the modulator section. With reference to Figure 7-17, examples of 50 percent and 100 percent undistorted modulation are depicted. In some cases, the cause of weak or distorted modulation is tracked down to a defective microphone. Modulator

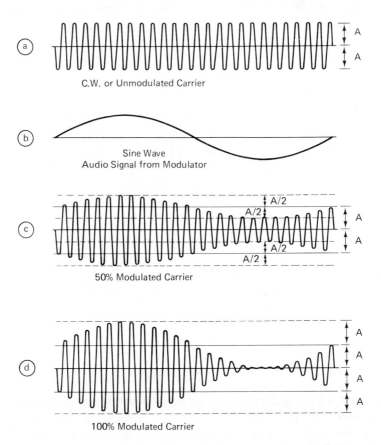

Fig. 7-17   Appearance of 50 and 100 percent modulated waveforms.

component or device faults can occur, which result in the same trouble symptoms or in distortion owing to overmodulation, as exemplified in Figure 7-18. Note that there are gaps along the zero-volt level in the modulation waveform, resulting from the fact that E_A has an excessive value. Another cause of distortion is nonlinear signal transfer resulting in dissymetry of the modulating waveform, as shown in Figure 7-19. These faults are evaluated to best advantage by signal tracing with the oscilloscope.

Diagnosis is made to best advantage with a sine-wave input to the microphone channel. A 1-kHz test frequency may be used. An audio generator may be connected in place of the microphone, or alternatively the generator may be used to energize a 2-in. speaker placed near the microphone. A typical CB transceiver develops 100 percent modulation with 0.5 volt of generator output signal. However, the manufacturer's specifications should be checked; various CB transceivers develop 100 percent modulation with as little as 0.3 volt, or as much as 5 volts, of generator output signal.

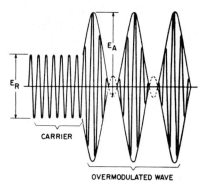

Fig. 7-18   **Example of distortion (sideband splatter) caused by carrier overmodulation.**

Fig. 7-19   **Distortion caused by dissymetry of the modulating waveform.**

7-8 Broadcast AM Receiver Diagnosis and Repair

A very useful diagnostic test for a "dead" broadcast AM receiver is depicted in Figure 7-20. A milliammeter is connected in series with the V_{cc} power-supply lead, and the meter reading is observed as the tuning dial is turned through its range. In normal operation, the current demands of the

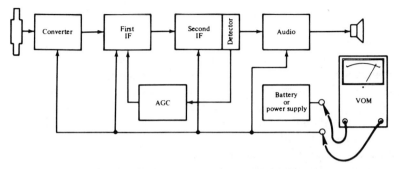

Fig. 7-20   Current-drain check for AM radio receiver.

IF stage and the output stage will normally change when a station is tuned in. If the volume control is turned to minimum, only the IF current drain owing to AGC action will be indicated by the meter. This change can be either an increase or a decrease depending on the type of AGC control that is utilized. Forward AGC results in a decrease of current drain when a station is tuned in; reverse AGC results in an increase of current drain when a station is tuned in. Thus, if there is no change in current drain when this diagnostic test is made, the repairman concludes that the trouble will be found in the high-frequency circuitry. Suppose that the volume control is advanced to maximum; in this case the current demand of the audio-output stage will normally dominate the change in meter reading. Most output stages have push-pull design and operate in class AB. Consequently, the meter reading will normally increase when a station is tuned in. If the technician observes that there is no change in meter variation when the volume control is turned from zero to its maximum setting, he concludes that the trouble will be found in the detector circuit or in the audio section. Normal variations in current demand for a receiver with reverse AGC are pictured in Figure 7-21.

When signal-injection tests are made to localize a defective stage, the order of tests is generally made as indicated in Figure 7-22. An AM signal generator is utilized as a signal source, and a 400-Hz (or 1-kHz) audio signal is first applied at the speaker input terminals. If an audio tone is heard from the speaker, the AF test signal is injected at point (2). An audible tone from the speaker indicates that the AF output amplifier is workable. An AF test signal is then injected at point (3). A modulated 455-kHz RF signal is injected at point (4), and then at point (5). A modulated RF test signal with a frequency equal to the tuning-dial setting is injected at point (6), then at point (7), and finally at point (8). If, for example, there is an audible tone from the speaker when the test signal is injected at point (6), but the speaker is silent when the signal is injected at point (7), the repairman concludes that there is a circuit fault in the RF amplifier.

Distortion can be analyzed to good advantage on the basis of scope waveform displays when the receiver is energized by a good quality AM signal generator. Clipping of the test signal at any of the test points noted in Figure 7-22 is a common form of distortion, and it indicates the occurrence of overload. Clipping in the IF section is likely to be the result of a defect in the AGC loop. Note in passing that this trouble symptom can result from replacing the detector diode and accidentally reversing its polarity. Again, a germanium diode should not be replaced with a silicon diode, or vice versa. If the radio receiver includes one or more short-wave bands, the input section indicated in Figure 7-22 requires more than one check. In other words, a signal of suitable frequency should be injected at point (8) on each setting of the band switch.

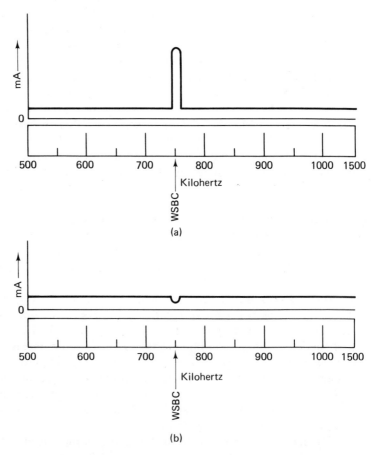

Fig. 7-21   **Current variation versus signal condition in normal operation.
(a) With volume control advanced; (b) with volume control turned down.**

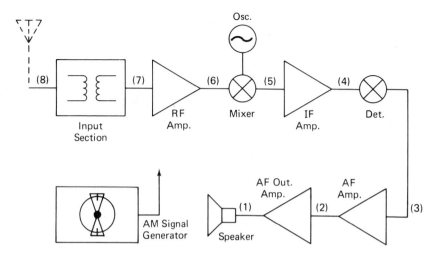

Fig. 7-22 **Order of signal-injection tests in a radio receiver.**

7-9 Broadcast FM Receiver Diagnosis and Repair

Most of the troubleshooting procedures that have been noted for AM radio receivers apply also to broadcast FM receivers. There are some differences that should be recognized by the repairman: for example, no AGC action is utilized in the IF section, and the last IF stage is always overdriven. The output signal from the last IF stage is normally clipped. Some FM receivers employ AGC in the RF section. Note that the bandwidth of the IF section in an FM receiver is 200 kHz, compared to 10 kHz in a broadcast AM receiver. An IF center frequency of 10.7 MHz is used in the FM IF section. Although an FM signal is required for signal-injection tests, a service-type AM generator can be used for this purpose because incidental frequency modulation is present along with the amplitude modulation in the output, particularly when the AM generator is set for a high percentage of modulation.

With reference to Figure 7-23, oscilloscope checks are not practical in the circuitry prior to integrated circuit U2, owing to the low levels of the signal in these sections. Accordingly, the FM front end and U1 would be checked by signal substitution. Observe that the stage-gain values are specified in dB power gain. In other words, these dB values cannot be checked directly with the dB scale on a voltmeter, because power gain in dB units involves the impedance of the circuit across which the voltmeter or oscilloscope is connected. As an illustration, note in Figure 7-23 that the input impedance to the FM front end is 300 ohms, the output impedance of the front end is 7 kΩ, the input impedance to U1 is 500 Ω, and the output impedance

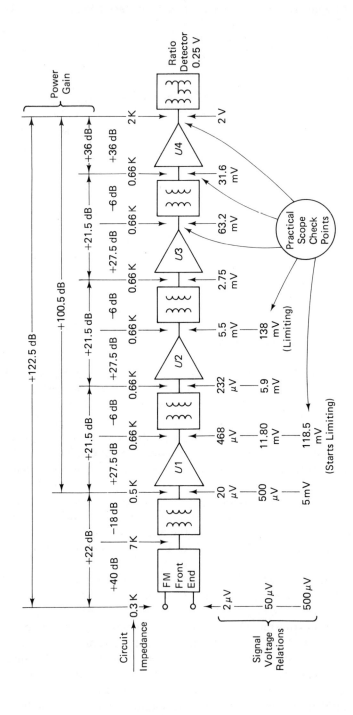

Fig. 7-23 Configuration, signal levels, and stage-gain values for a typical FM tuner with integrated circuits.

of U1 is 600 Ω. In turn, the dB power level at each of these points is a function both of the signal voltage and of the circuit impedance at that point. Accordingly, the repairman is more concerned with signal-voltage levels than with signal-power levels.

The tuned circuits indicated in Figure 7-23 must be in correct alignment for normal operation of the signal channel. Alignment instructions are generally issued by the manufacturer. A generalized FM receiver sweep-alignment setup is shown in Figure 7-24. Observe that the bandwidth of the IF response curve is 200 kHz, and normally extends from 10.6 MHz to 10.8 MHz. The FM demodulator response curve has a peak-to-peak excursion (bandwidth) of 200 kHz, from 10.6 MHz to 10.8 MHz, with a center frequency of 10.7 MHz. A marker generator is utilized with the sweep generator to display a vertical "pip" on the response curve at the frequency to which the marker generator is set. A frequency marker (pip) identifies any chosen frequency point along the response curve. Note that the IF response curve is displayed when the oscilloscope is connected at the input to the FM detector. The FM demodulator response curve is displayed when the oscilloscope is connected at the output of the FM detector.

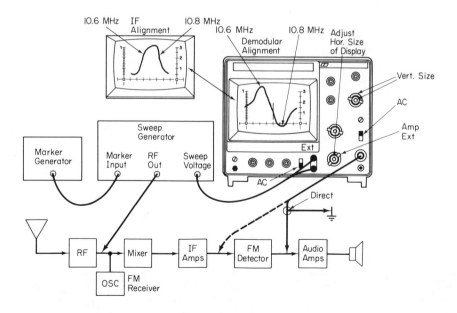

Fig. 7-24   FM receiver sweep-alignment setup. (Courtesy, B&K Precision, Division of Dynascan Corp.)

Review Questions

1. Name the three basic types of radio equipment with which the electronic repairman is concerned.

2. State three basic radio diagnostic tests.

3. Do service-type AM signal generators ordinarily provide a pure sine-wave output?

4. Explain the basic distinction between the single-conversion and the dual-conversion superheterodyne arrangement.

5. What is the most likely cause of off-frequency transmission in a CB transceiver?

6. How is a current-variation test made in preliminary diagnosis of a "dead" AM broadcast receiver?

7. Compare the bandwidth of an AM broadcast receiver with that of an FM broadcast receiver.

8. Briefly explain a sweep-alignment setup for an FM radio receiver.

9. What is the center frequency of a standard FM IF amplifier?

10. How are frequency markers developed on a response curve?

Chapter 8

Black-and-White Television Receiver Repair

8-1 TV Receiver Parameters

A TV receiver in normal operating condition has the approximate video signal-channel gain values noted in Figure 8-1. A total signal-voltage gain of 50,000 times is provided. The signal voltages have basic waveshapes as illustrated in Figure 8-2. From the viewpoint of the technician, receiver waveforms can be grouped into four categories:

1. Picture signal
2. Sound signal
3. Control signal
4. Internally generated waveforms.

The picture signal is also called the camera signal, and it is combined with the horizontal and vertical sync control signals. This composite video signal is accompanied by the sound signal. The horizontal and vertical sweep waveforms are internally generated and are controlled by the sync signals. Horizontal-AFC waveforms are a combination of control and internally generated signals. The general arrangement of the picture and sound channels is shown in Figure 8-3. Experienced technicians know that the waveshape of the horizontal sync pulse can provide considerable preliminary information concerning the functioning of the picture channel. For example, with reference to Figure 8-4, a normal overall frequency response for the signal channel (plus linear amplification) results in display of a horizontal sync pulse with normal proportions and square corners. Note that it is desirable to use a good-quality video signal generator in this type of diagnosis; in other words, an off-the-air signal will not necessarily provide an undistorted sync pulse. In particular, network program transmissions often have deteriorated sync pulses.

8-2 Sync Pulse Displays

In case that the RF, IF, or video-amplifier section has subnormal bandwidth, the sync pulse will be displayed with rounded corners. Or, if the overall frequency characteristic has a rising high-frequency response, the displayed sync pulse will exhibit tilt and overshoots. On the other hand, in the event that the overall frequency response has low frequency attenuation, the sync pulse will be displayed with an opposite tilt and no overshoot. Sometimes the IF section develops regeneration with the result that the horizontal sync pulse is highly distorted and is displayed as a group of uneven pulses. Subnormal bandwidth is a common deficiency in receivers that have not been carefully aligned; comparative sync-pulse displays are pictured in Figure 8-5. Observe that the rise time of the pulse is also slowed down in a channel that has subnormal bandwidth. Rapid rise time requires the passage of comparatively high frequencies.

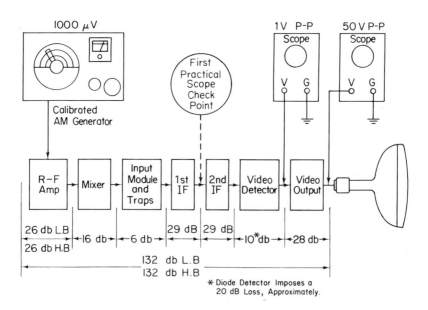

Fig. 8-1   Video signal channel gains for a typical TV receiver.

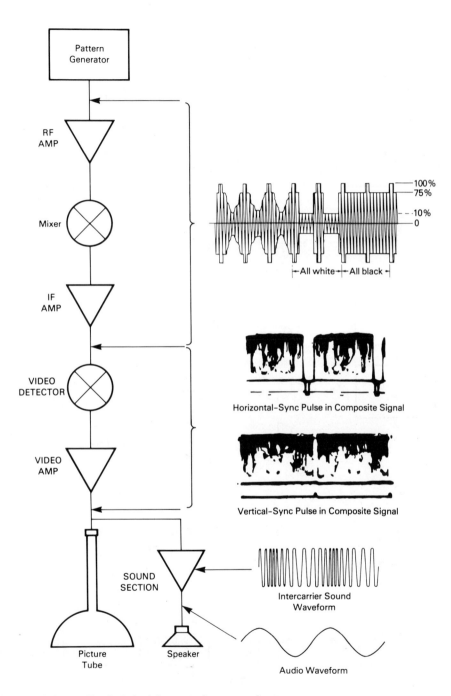

Fig. 8-2   Basic television receiver waveforms.

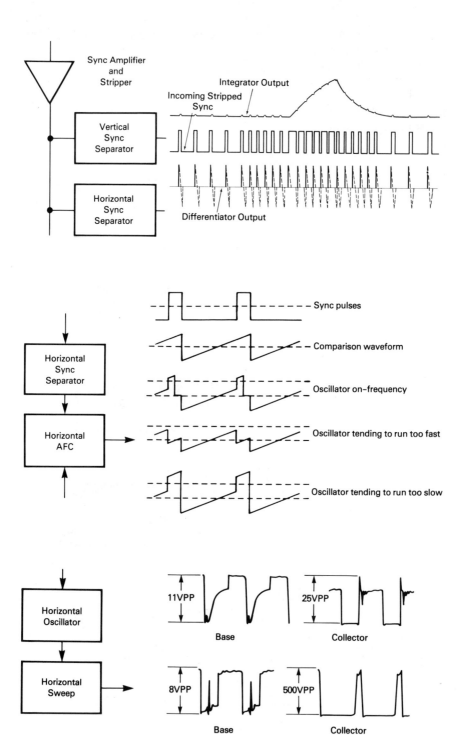

Fig. 8-2   Continued.

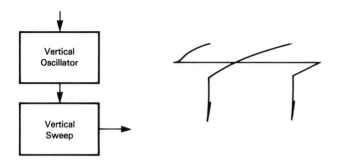

Fig. 8-2 **Continued.**

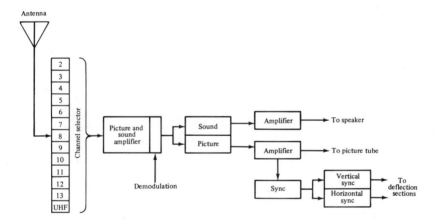

Fig. 8-3 **General arrangement of the picture and sound channels.**

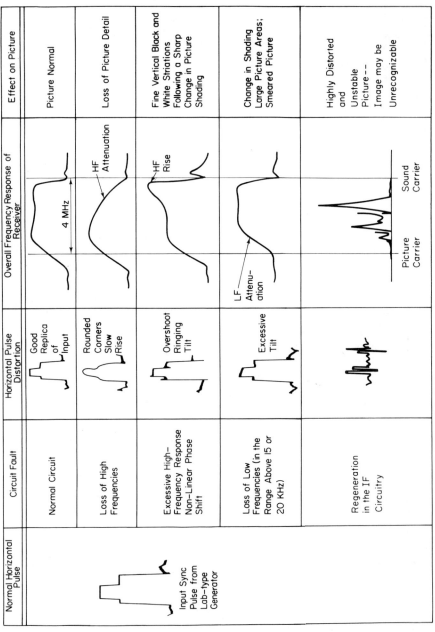

Fig. 8-4   Sync-pulse distortion versus IF channel bandwidth and amplitude response.

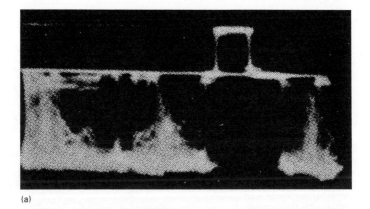

(a)

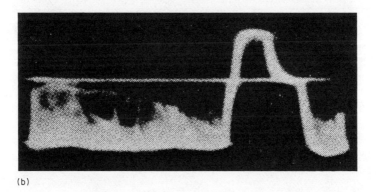

(b)

Fig. 8-5   **Comparative sync-pulse displays. (a) Output from receiver with full overall frequency response; (b) output from receiver with subnormal overall frequency response.**

If the bias voltage is incorrect or the collector voltage is subnormal on the video-amplifier transistor, for example, the sync pulse may become compressed or clipped, as shown in Figure 8-6. Partial compression of the sync tip can result in unstable sync lock, and complete compression or clipping of the sync tip results in loss of horizontal sync lock. The bias voltage on a transistor may be either subnormal or abnormal. Thus, the sync pulse may be properly displayed, but the camera signal may be compressed, as pictured in Figure 8-7. Note that if the camera signal contains peak-white information (as in a test-pattern signal), the sync tip normally occupies 25 percent of the total composite video signal amplitude. Observe in Figure 8-7 that the sync tip occupies 42 percent of the total waveform amplitude. Because the white information in the signal is compressed, this trouble condition is called white compression.

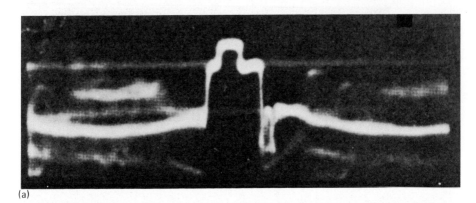

(a)

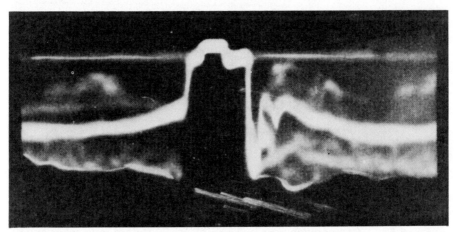

(b)

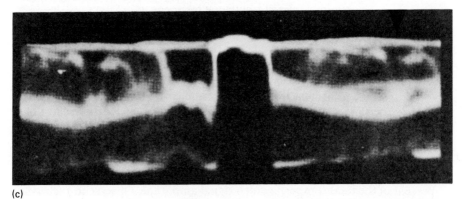

(c)

Fig. 8-6 **Progressive sync compression. (a) Horizontal sync pulse with noticeable compression; (b) sync pulse with severe compression; (c) sync tip virtually absent (clipped).**

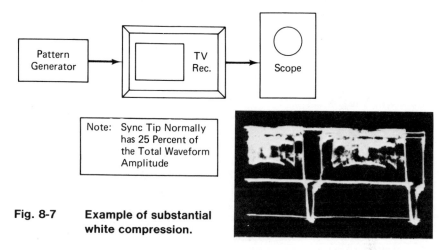

Note: Sync Tip Normally has 25 Percent of the Total Waveform Amplitude

Fig. 8-7 **Example of substantial white compression.**

8-3 Signal Tracing in TV Circuitry

Signal tracing in the IF section must be accomplished with a demodulator probe connected to the oscilloscope, owing to the comparatively high IF frequency (43 MHz). Even if the oscilloscope has high sensitivity, it is impractical to check the low-level signal at the tuner output. Accordingly, the technician makes a tuner-substitution test in case he suspects that the tuner is defective. A demodulator probe can be used to check for presence or absence of IF signal from the output of the first IF stage to the input of the picture detector. Note that stage gain cannot be measured with a demodulator probe owing to the circuit disturbance that the probe imposes. Also, the waveform displayed on the oscilloscope screen is not a useful indication of the IF signal waveform because of the extensive high-frequency attenuation that occurs in the probe. As noted in Figure 8-8, its modulated signal range extends only to 5 kHz. In turn, the display provided on the oscilloscope screen is essentially the vertical sync pulse with a residue of horizontal pulses and camera signal. The probe strips the equalizing pulses from the waveform and does not reproduce the serrations in the vertical sync pulse.

When the video signal is traced through the video-amplifier section, a low-capacitance (C) probe should be connected to the oscilloscope. A low-C probe minimizes circuit disturbance and permits display of the true sync pulse waveform. Of course, the same consideration applies to analysis of keying pulses, comparison waveforms, and sweep waveforms. A low-C probe ensures that circuit loading will be minimized and that undistorted waveforms will be displayed. Waveform analysis includes peak-to-peak voltage measurements, in addition to waveshape verification. TV receiver service data customarily specifies peak-to-peak voltage values for key waveforms. These are not absolute amplitude values, but are subject to a toler-

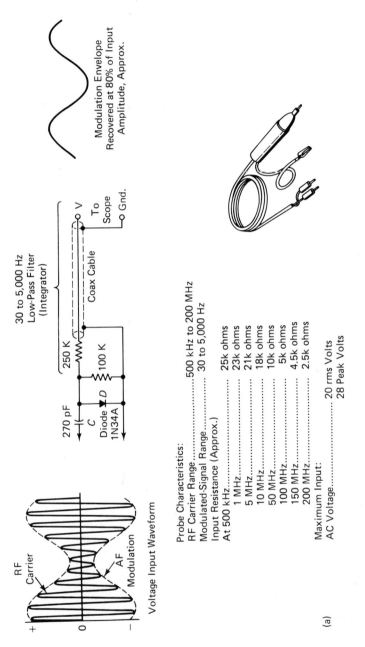

Modulation Envelope Recovered at 80% of Input Amplitude, Approx.

30 to 5,000 Hz Low-Pass Filter (Integrator)

250 K

270 pF

C

Diode D 1N34A

100 K

Coax Cable

V To Scope
Gnd.

RF Carrier

AF Modulation

Voltage Input Waveform

Probe Characteristics:
RF Carrier Range............................500 kHz to 200 MHz
Modulated-Signal Range................30 to 5,000 Hz
Input Resistance (Approx.)
  At 500 kHz...........................25k ohms
  1 MHz...............................23k ohms
  5 MHz...............................21k ohms
  10 MHz..............................18k ohms
  50 MHz..............................10k ohms
  100 MHz.............................5k ohms
  150 MHz.............................4.5k ohms
  200 MHz.............................2.5k ohms

Maximum Input:
  AC Voltage...........................20 rms Volts
                                       28 Peak Volts

(a)

Fig. 8-8 Demodulator probes. (a) Conventional demodulator probe and characteristics; (b) medium-impedance demodulator probe that can display horizontal sync pulses; (c) simplest form of demodulator probe.

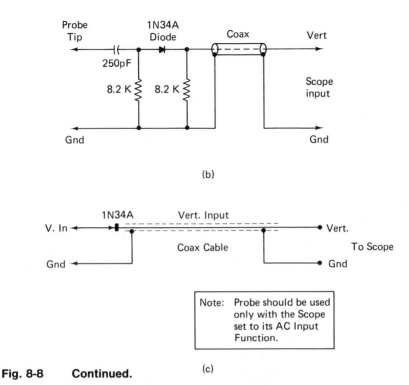

(b)

Note: Probe should be used only with the Scope set to its AC Input Function.

(c)

Fig. 8-8   Continued.

ance of ±20 percent. As an illustration, the repairman would regard an amplitude in the range of 80 to 120 volts as acceptable for a waveform with a specified amplitude of 100 volts. The polarity of a waveform is usually specified also. For example, the composite video waveform may have either a positive or a negative polarity specification, as seen in Figure 8-9. If a detector diode is replaced with incorrect polarity, the video waveform will be inverted, a negative picture will be displayed, and sync action will become very unstable.

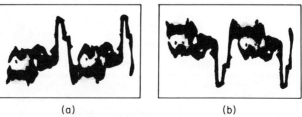

(a)   (b)

Fig. 8-9   Display of the composite video waveform. (a) Positive-going sync pulses; (b) negative-going sync pulses.

Horizontal sync pulses are displayed when the oscilloscope is operated at a 15,750-Hz deflection rate, or submultiples thereof. On the other hand, if the oscilloscope is operated at a 60-Hz deflection rate or at a submultiple, the vertical sync pulse is displayed, as exemplified in Figure 8-10. Note that the vertical sync appears as only a narrow interval in the video signal unless the horizontal-gain control of the oscilloscope is advanced. Hum voltage sometimes contaminates the video signal, as shown in Figure 8-10(b). It produces "hum bars" in the picture and can also impair sync action. When this trouble symptom occurs, suspicion is directed to the filter section of the power supply. In old-model tube-type receivers, hum symptoms can also be caused by heater-cathode leakage in the video-amplifier tube, for example.

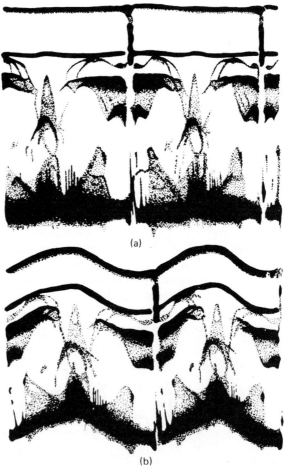

(a)

(b)

Fig. 8-10   Appearance of 60-Hz hum voltage in a frame-rate TV video signal. (a) Scope display without hum interference; (b) scope display with hum interference.

8-4 Sweep Alignment Procedure

Tuned circuitry in television receivers comprises VHF coupling circuits, IF coupling and trap circuits, sound-takeoff circuits, and intercarrier-sound circuits. Local-oscillator circuits are also tuned. Sweep alignment techniques are used because the tuned circuits have considerable bandwidth. Basic frequency-response curve development with a sweep generator and oscilloscope is shown in Figure 8-11. The sweep generator applies a large-deviation frequency-modulated signal to the tuned circuitry for display of its amplitude-vs.-frequency characteristic. This FM sweep signal has a repetition rate of 60 Hz. A detector follows the tuned circuits, and the detector output is applied to an oscilloscope. The detector demodulates the IF sweep voltage, and a demodulated frequency-response curve is displayed on the oscilloscope screen. Most sweep-alignment generators have built-in marker generators. A marker generator mixes a sine-wave signal of precise frequency with the sweep signal. In turn, a beating action occurs between

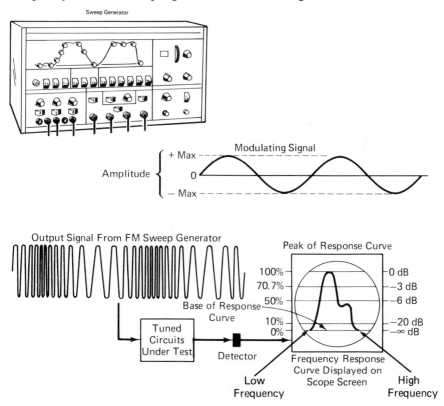

Fig. 8-11 FM sweep signal develops the frequency response curve of the tuned circuits under test.

the two signals, and a marker indication (also termed a "pip" or a "birdie") appears on the curve at the marker frequency (Figure 8-12). Relative amplitudes on the curve may be designated either in percentage-of-maximum response, or in decibel units.

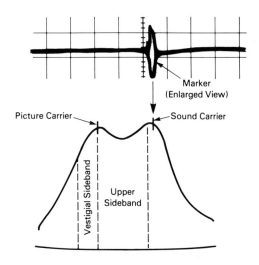

Fig. 8-12   Specified frequency-response curve for an RF tuner.

Observe in Figure 8-11 that the output signal from the FM sweep generator has a relatively high frequency, such as 43 MHz, and that if the detector were omitted, no pattern would be displayed on the scope screen. In other words, the 43-MHz center frequency of the test signal exceeds the response capability of the oscilloscope's vertical amplifier. When the response curve of a VHF tuner is checked, the test frequency is in the order of 100 MHz; accordingly, the signal must be demodulated before it is fed to the oscilloscope. With reference to Figure 8-13, a mixer transistor is operated over a nonlinear portion of its transfer characteristic. In turn, a mixer has detector action; when an oscilloscope is connected at the output of the mixer transistor, a demodulated VHF response curve is displayed on the oscilloscope screen. After a sweep-alignment signal is demodulated, the oscilloscope is required only to respond to the envelope frequency of the pattern, which is roughly comparable to a 60-Hz square wave. Since any service-type oscilloscope responds adequately in this frequency range, a wide-band oscilloscope is not required in conventional alignment procedures.

Each channel of a front end (RF tuner) should be checked for correct frequency response, and alignment adjustments should be made in accordance with the receiver service data. Picture-carrier, sound-carrier, and local-

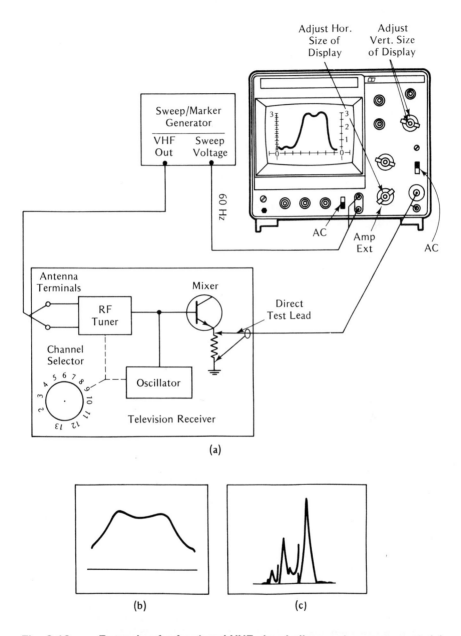

Fig. 8-13 Example of a front-end VHF visual-alignment arrangement. (a) Test setup; (b) normal RF-tuner frequency-response curve; (c) a regeneratively distorted frequency-response curve. (Courtesy, B&K Precision, Division of Dynascan Corp.)

oscillator frequencies for each VHF channel are noted in Figure 8-14. As a practical note, it is often desirable to disable the local oscillator during tuner alignment procedures. That is, the oscillator frequency and its harmonics may beat with the sweep signal and marker signal frequencies with production of spurious marker indications on the frequency-response curve. The local oscillator may be easily disabled by temporarily connecting a bypass capacitor from the base of the oscillator transistor to ground. It is often desirable also to clamp the AGC line to the tuner at its nominal voltage value with a suitable bias battery. Unless the AGC line is clamped, reaction from the AGC section may tend to distort the displayed frequency-response curve.

When the tuner response curve cannot be brought into accordance with specifications (allowing for reasonable tolerances), the repairman concludes that a malfunction is present. Open or leaky capacitors are common culprits, although transistors may also become defective. Corroded and worn switch contacts may also cause trouble symptoms. Most tuners are designed in the manner exemplified in Figure 8-15. Note that the VHF frequency-response curve is shaped by adjustment of L8 and C10. These are compromise adjustments, since the individual turret coils such as L13 and L14 are not adjustable. In turn, the technician must "split the difference" between channel responses. Note also that L17 operates at IF frequency and is not adjusted during the VHF alignment procedure. Oscillator frequencies are adjusted in a separate procedure after the frequency-response curves have been contoured. A basic oscillator-frequency adjustment is provided by L16; in addition, the fine-tuning control enables oscillator-frequency trimming on each channel (for example, L15).

8-5 IF Circuitry Tests

An IF frequency-response curve is displayed with the test setup depicted in Figure 8-16. The sweep-and-marker test signals are applied to the base of the mixer transistor. A suitable AGC bias override voltage is applied to the AGC line to stabilize the IF gain and thereby avoid distortion of the displayed response curve. Note that the oscilloscope is connected through a 100-kΩ resistor to the output terminal of the video detector. This resistor provides low-pass filter action with respect to the capacitance of the vertical-input cable, and develops sharp marker indication. It is often called an isolating resistor. IF response curves have an allowable tolerance of ± 10 percent. Greater deviations point to off-value components or defective devices in the IF network.

A three-stage IF amplifier configuration is shown in Figure 8-17. The principal alignment adjustments are T2, T3, and T4; T1 and T2 function as traps. A gain of 18 dB is normally provided by the second stage and by the third stage; the first stage normally has a gain ranging from unity to 40 dB, depending upon the value of the AGC bias voltage. Note that clamp diode

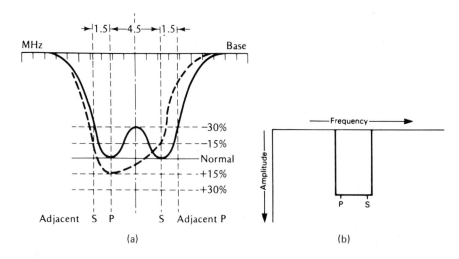

Frequency Reference Chart

Channel Number	Picture Carrier Frequency (MHz)	Sound Carrier Frequency (MHz)	Receiver VHF Oscillator Frequency (MHz)
2	55.25	59.75	101
3	61.25	65.75	107
4	67.25	71.75	113
5	77.25	81.75	123
6	83.25	87.75	129
7	175.25	179.75	221
8	181.25	185.75	227
9	187.25	191.75	233
10	193.25	197.75	239
11	199.25	203.75	245
12	205.25	209.75	251
13	211.25	215.75	257

(c)

Fig. 8-14 **VHF tuner response curve frequencies and tolerances. (a) Representative curve with permissible tolerances; (b) ideal response curve; (c) picture-carrier, sound-carrier, and local-oscillator frequencies.**

CR1 prevents the collector current from falling to zero at any time, so that Q1 cannot be completely cut off. Observe also that the first IF tuned circuit is the mixer tank (not shown), of which L1 is a part. L1's total impedance is in the order of 1000 ohms, which assists in developing the necessary wide-

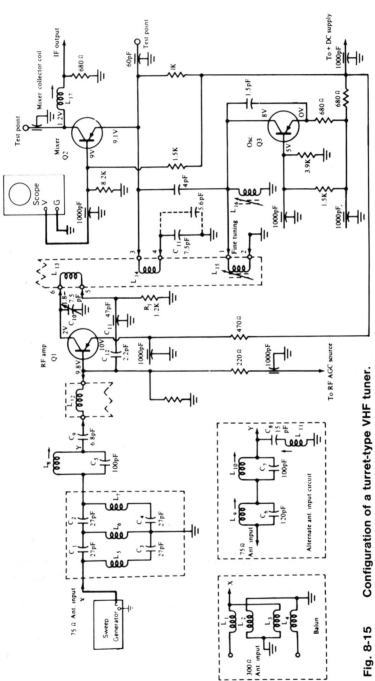

Fig. 8-15   Configuration of a turret-type VHF tuner.

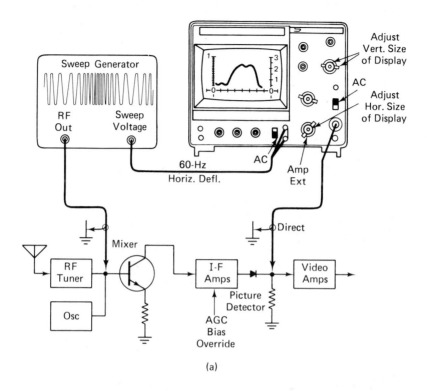

(a)

Fig. 8-16 IF alignment procedure. (a) Equipment connections; (b) representative response curve with permissible tolerances; (c) ideal IF response curve. (Continued on next page)

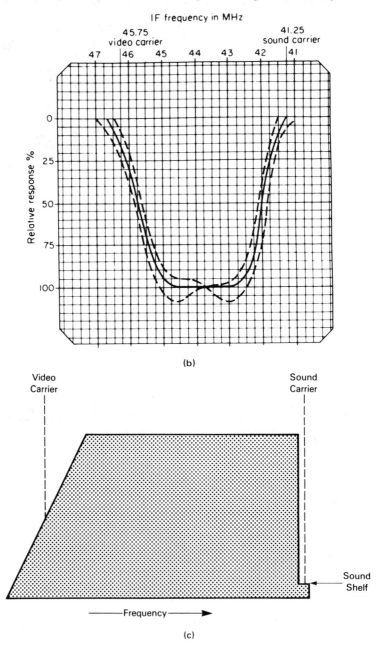

(b)

(c)

Fig. 8-16 Continued.

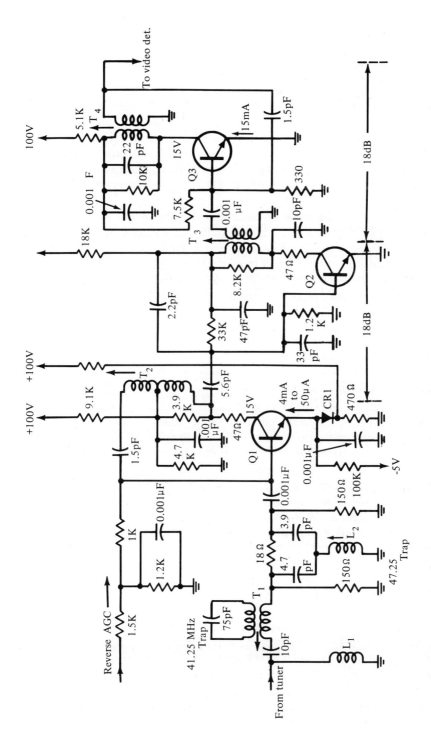

Fig. 8-17   A three-stage video-IF amplifier configuration.

band response for the channel. Trap T1 normally reduces the IF response amplitude to about 10 percent of its maximum value at 41.25 MHz. No adjacent-channel picture trap is provided in this example. L2 operates as an adjacent-channel sound trap.

Observe that the collector load circuit T2 in Figure 8-17 is center-tapped; it feeds out-of-phase signal voltage back to the base of Q1 via a 1.5-pF capacitor. This is a neutralizing circuit for stabilization of the first IF stage. Q1 normally operates with approximately 15-V collector potential and normally draws about 4 mA of emitter current. However, under strong-signal conditions, AGC bias action can cause the collector current to fall as low as 50 μA. The dynamic range of Q1 is approximately 40 dB. Under strong-signal conditions, CR1 becomes reverse-biased. T2 is shunted by resistance to reduce the stage Q value and thereby obtain adequate bandwidth. The RC network between the base and collector of Q2 comprises both a bias source and a negative-feedback path. Wide-band response is thereby obtained with a tradeoff in gain. Q3 provides a comparatively high signal-power level inasmuch as a video detector requires appreciable power input. About 15 mA of emitter current is normally drawn by Q3.

8-6 IF Regeneration and Oscillation

IF regeneration or oscillation is occasionally encountered by the diagnostician. When IF regeneration is present, the frequency-response curve becomes highly distorted. Or, if the IF strip breaks into oscillation, there is no signal passage; the chief symptom of IF oscillation is a high DC voltage measured at the output of the picture detector whether a signal is present or absent. IF regeneration or oscillation is commonly caused by a defective neutralizing capacitor; this malfunction also results from serious misalignment. If a conventional IF transistor is accidentally replaced with a high-beta type, regeneration or oscillation may occur. Open decoupling or bypass capacitors in the IF network can also permit positive feedback. When components or devices are replaced, it is often essential to observe their original mounting positions, orientations, and lead lengths. Otherwise, unsuspected coupling may be introduced with development of regeneration or oscillation.

8-7 Video-Amplifier Tests

Note the standard method used to check video-amplifier frequency response, shown in Figure 8-18. A video-frequency sweep signal (zero to 4.5 MHz) is applied to the input of the video amplifier. Because the video amplifier is not followed by a detector, the usual procedure is to utilize a demodulator probe with the oscilloscope (Figure 8-8). The demodulator probe develops the envelope of the video-frequency sweep signal, and the video amplifier frequency-response curve is displayed on the oscilloscope screen.

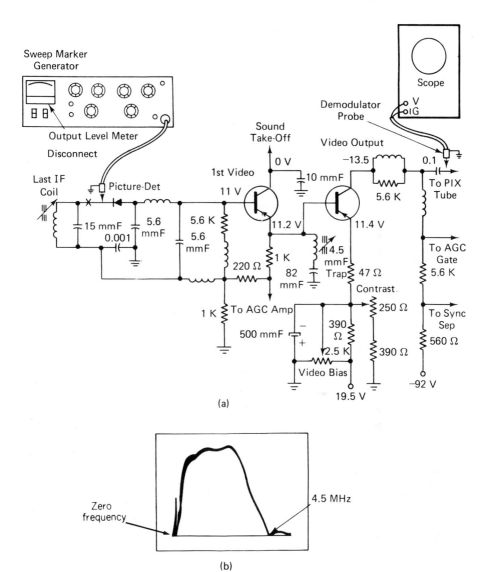

Fig. 8-18   Standard method of checking the frequency response of the video amplifier. (a) Test setup; (b) typical response curve.

A video-frequency sweep generator may provide beat markers or absorption markers (Figure 8-19). When beat-frequency markers are utilized, a post-injection section is usually included in the generator. A post-injector arrangement combines the marker signal with the sweep signal after the sweep signal has passed through the video amplifier. In turn, possible spurious in-

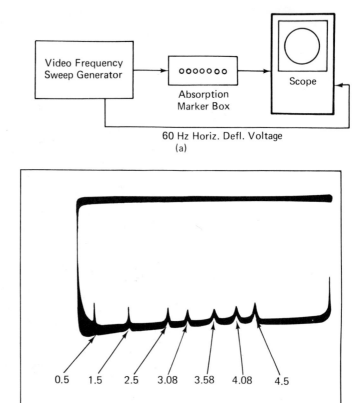

60 Hz Horiz. Defl. Voltage
(a)

(b)

Fig. 8-19 **Absorption markers on the demodulated output from a video-frequency sweep generator. (a) Test connections; (b) pattern.**

terharmonic beats are avoided. An absorption marker has no associated generator signal, and no interharmonic beats can occur.

8-8 Intercarrier Sound System

An example of an intercarrier sound-IF configuration is shown in Figure 8-20. Alignment of the sound-IF amplifier is made in the same basic manner that was noted previously for FM receivers. However, the intercarrier-sound section in a TV receiver has a center frequency of 4.5 MHz, whereas the IF section in an FM receiver has a center frequency of 10.7 MHz. Frequency interrelations of the black-and-white TV picture- and sound-channel sections are pictured in Figure 8-21. Most of the gain and selectivity in the picture channel is provided by the IF section. Most of the

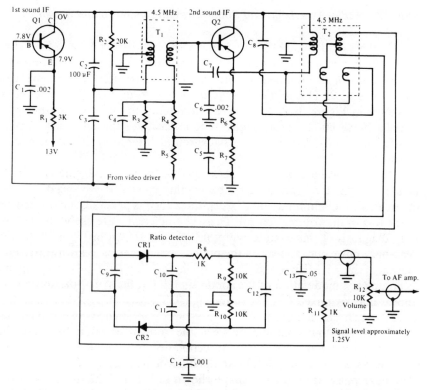

Fig. 8-20   Typical intercarrier sound-IF and ratio-detector configuration.

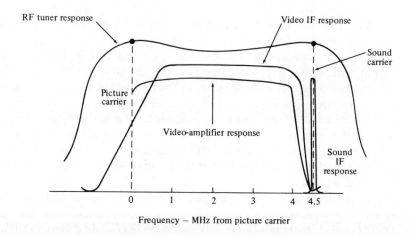

Frequency — MHz from picture carrier

Fig. 8-21   Frequency interrelations of the black-and-white TV picture- and sound-channel sections.

gain in the sound channel is provided by the intercarrier-IF amplifier. Improper alignment or overload in the picture channel can result in improper signal ratios or in nonlinear amplification, with resulting development of 60-Hz sync buzz. Three types of sync-buzz waveforms may be encountered, as shown in Figure 8-22. Sync-buzz interference in the sound output produces a harsh 60-Hz rasping tone. The intensity of the buzz may remain steady, or it may vary with the background brightness of the displayed picture.

Vertical-sweep buzz occurs occasionally. In most cases, the amplitude of a sync-buzz tone increases as the volume control is advanced. On the other hand, the amplitude of a sweep-buzz tone is generally unaffected by the setting of the volume control. These characteristics are useful in preliminary diagnosis of this trouble symptom. As was shown in Figure 8-22, the sync-buzz pulse may appear on the oscilloscope screen as a downward modulation of the 4.5-MHz sound signal. Again, the sync-buzz pulse may appear as an upward modulation of the sound signal. Or, the sync-buzz pulse may appear linearly mixed with the sound signal. The tone of sync-buzz interference is much the same as that of sweep-buzz interference. Sweep buzz derives from spurious coupling between the vertical-sweep section and the sound section. Sometimes the audio section becomes coupled into the vertical-sweep system as the result of an open decoupling or bypass capacitor. A sync-buzz pulse has the basic shape shown in Figure 8-22 (it derives from the vertical-sync interval). On the other hand, a sweep-buzz pulse has a spike shape.

8-9 Horizontal-Output Section Tests

Consider the horizontal-output arrangement shown in Figure 8-23. Note that the high-voltage (flyback) transformer, yoke, and damper (D105) operate as an emitter-follower load for Q102. As seen in Figure 8-24, the output transformer goes into conduction at the center of the forward-scan interval and produces a linear ramp for the last half of the scan. Then, at the end of the scan, Q102 is abruptly turned off by the driver waveform, and a high-amplitude "flyback pulse" is generated. This is the flyback or retrace interval that returns the electron beam to the left-hand edge of the picture-tube screen and causes damper D105 to conduct. In turn, the damper continues to conduct for the first half of the forward-scan interval, after which it goes into nonconduction.

To protect the horizontal-output transistor against the possibility of excessive current flow, a current-limiting resistor Q108 is included. Also, diode D107 bypasses high-amplitude spike voltages that could damage Q108. The high-voltage supply for the picture tube is developed by stepping up the flyback pulse through T102. In turn, a 13-kV pulse is developed, which is rectified and applied to the ultor (high-voltage electrode) of the picture tube. Meanwhile, the flyback pulse is also rectified by D508 and filtered to pro-

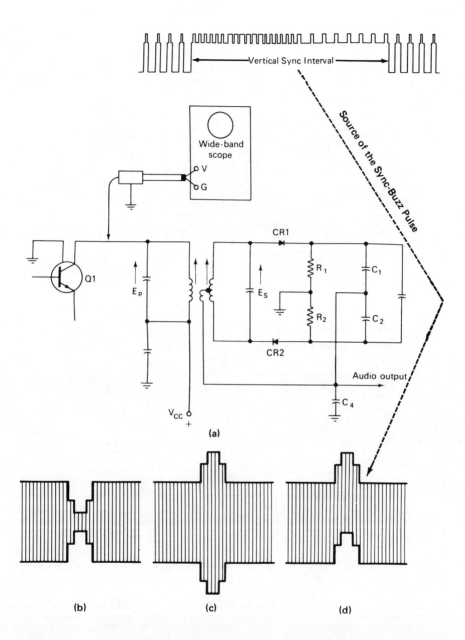

Fig. 8-22   Three types of sync-buzz waveforms. (a) Test setup; (b) downward modulation; (c) upward modulation; (d) linear mixture.

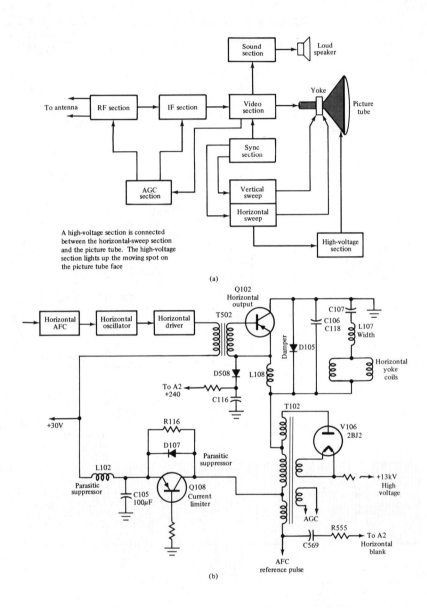

Fig. 8-23   Basic horizontal-output configuration. (a) Block diagram; (b) skeleton circuitry.

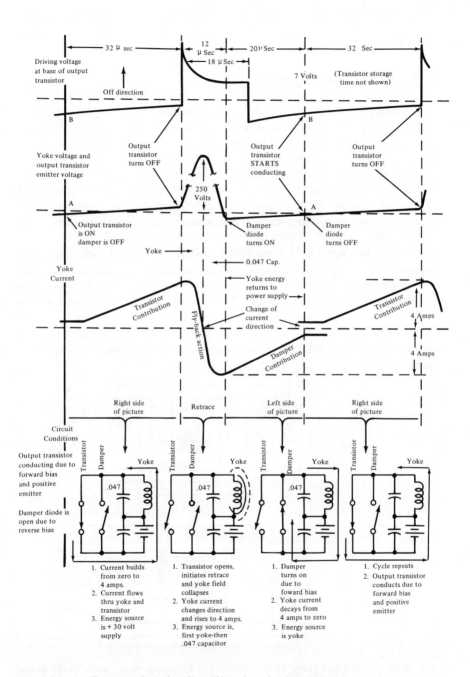

Fig. 8-24   Progressive circuit actions in a horizontal-output system.

vide +240 volts to the accelerating anode of the picture tube. The flyback transformer also supplies an AGC keying pulse and a comparison pulse for the AFC section.

8-10 Picture-Tube Brighteners

When the picture tube display lacks sufficient brightness, the repairman can sometimes obtain additional screen brightness by operating the heater at a somewhat higher voltage than rated. A higher voltage results in greater heat radiation and increases the cathode temperature. In turn, increased electron emission can often be obtained from the cathode, and the increased beam current that results will produce a brighter picture on the screen. This brightness increase may not persist for more than a short period, although there are cases in which considerable extension of useful picture-tube life has been obtained. Two types of picture-tube brighteners are in general use, as depicted in Figure 8-25. One design, called the isolated type, has a two-winding transformer construction, and the secondary provides a fixed voltage for the heater. The other design, termed the autotransformer type, has a low-boost and a high-boost switch. The isolated type has an advantage that it will also eliminate the shading effect of heater-cathode leakage in the electron gun. The autotransformer type has an advantage in that extra-high boost voltage is available to obtain additional service from a failing tube.

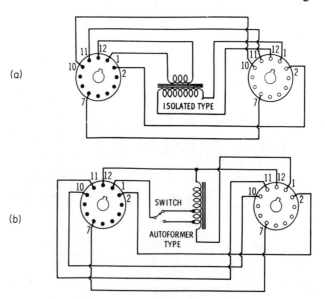

Fig. 8-25   Picture-tube brighteners. (a) Isolated type, with fixed boost voltage; (b) autotransformer type, with low-boost and high-boost voltages.

Review Questions

1. What three basic signals are included in a TV broadcast transmission?
2. Where is the first practical scope check point in a TV IF strip?
3. How does subnormal signal-channel bandwidth affect TV picture reproduction?
4. Explain the operation of a demodulator probe.
5. Why does a low-capacitance probe facilitate waveform checks in high-impedance circuitry?
6. Where is the oscilloscope connected in a front-end visual-alignment setup?
7. What is the approximate center frequency of a standard TV IF strip?
8. How does a TV repairman check for the presence of IF oscillation?
9. Describe the appearance of an absorption marker.
10. Explain the development of sync buzz in a TV receiver.

Chapter 9

Color Television
Receiver Repair

9-1 Color Receiver Parameters

A color-TV receiver employs the circuit sections that have been discussed for black-and-white receivers, plus chroma (color processing) circuitry, color-sync circuits, and picture-tube convergence configurations. A general block diagram for solid-state color-TV receivers is shown in Figure 9-1. Although there are more functional sections to contend with in a color receiver than in a black-and-white receiver, the same basic electrical and electronic principles apply. From a general viewpoint, the chroma section can be regarded as an elaboration of the video-amplifier section. One refinement that the technician encounters in the chroma section is the processing of three-phase signal voltages. However, only an extension of fundamental video-signal characteristics is involved. The color-sync section is more analogous to the horizontal-AFC section in a black-and-white receiver than to the sync-clipper and separator sections.

9-2 Color Receiver Waveforms

Basic color-TV system waveforms are noted in Figure 9-2. Note that the complete color signal comprises the horizontal and vertical sync pulses, the color burst, the Y signal, and the chroma signal (along with the FM sound signal). The color burst has a function analogous to that of the sync pulses in that it operates to maintain color sync lock. It has a frequency of

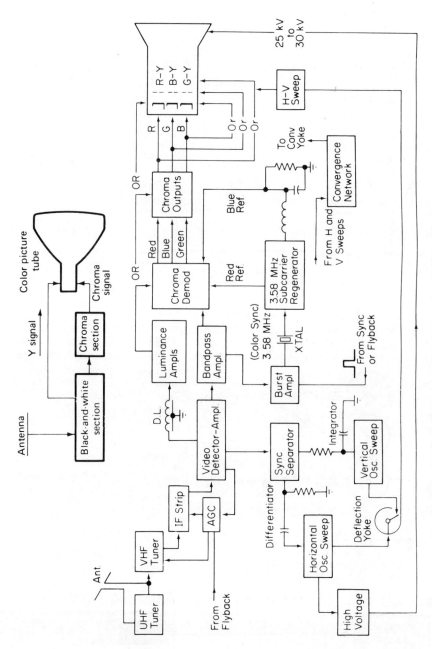

Fig. 9-1   General block diagram for a solid-state color-TV receiver.

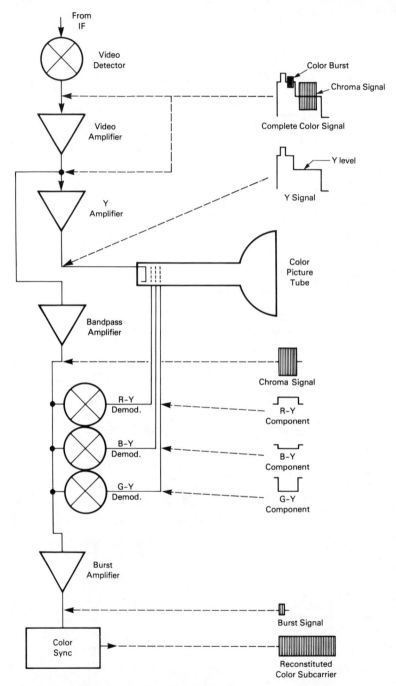

Fig. 9-2   Basic color-TV system waveforms.

3.58 MHz and is generically a sample of the color subcarrier that was suppressed at the color-TV transmitter. At the receiver, this color burst is processed to lock in the receiver's color-subcarrier oscillator, whereby the subcarrier is reconstituted (regenerated) and is then reinserted into the chroma signal. The chroma signal has a band width of approximately 1 MHz. It comprises upper and lower sideband frequencies only, inasmuch as the subcarrier frequency was previously suppressed at the transmitter. The Y signal is the same as the camera signal or video signal in a black-and-white TV system. (See Figure 9-3.)

Note that the Y amplifier in a color-TV receiver has a low-pass filter action that effectively separates the Y signal from the complete color signal.

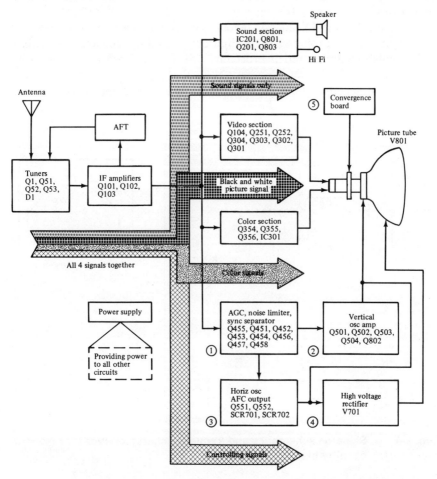

Fig. 9-3 Block diagram with signal-flow identification. (Courtesy, Heath Co.)

On the other hand, the bandpass amplifier has a high-pass filter action that effectively separates the chroma signal from the complete color signal. Skeleton schematics are shown in Figure 9-4. The burst signal is separated from the chroma signal by the burst amplifier. As noted above, the chroma signal has three phases that are associated with reproduction of red, green, and blue colors; phase angles are maintained with reference to the color subcarrier. These phases are termed the R-Y, G-Y, and B-Y phases. They are separated from one another by three chroma demodulators (detectors), which are phase-amplitude detectors. The color subcarrier frequency is locally generated by a subcarrier oscillator and split into the three appropriate phases for injection into the chroma demodulators. Outputs from the three chroma demodulators are mixed with the Y signal, either in the color picture tube, or in a separate matrix section.

A typical color-TV chassis layout (General Electric 19YC) is shown with right and left profile views in Figure 9-5. Modular construction is featured, which facilitates repair procedures. Seven replaceable modules contain most of the receiver circuitry. Note that the dynamic convergence module is attached to the upper right area of the metal chassis frame, and

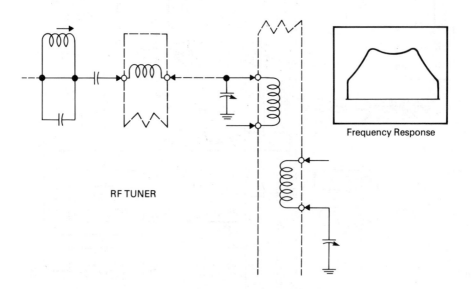

Frequency Response

RF TUNER

Fig. 9-4 **Skeleton schematics and frequency characteristics for resonant circuitry in color-TV receivers.**

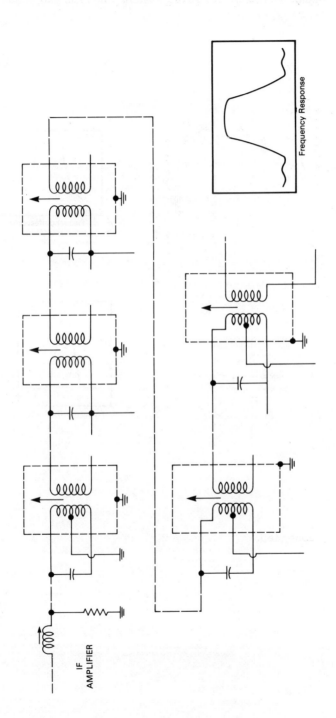

Frequency Response

IF AMPLIFIER

Fig. 9-4 continued.

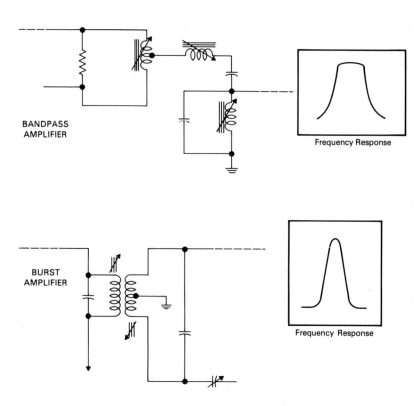

BANDPASS
AMPLIFIER

Frequency Response

BURST
AMPLIFIER

Frequency Response

Fig. 9-4   continued.

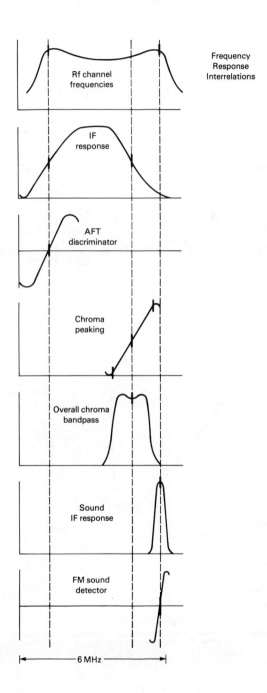

Frequency
Response
Interrelations

Rf channel
frequencies

IF
response

AFT
discriminator

Chroma
peaking

Overall chroma
bandpass

Sound
IF response

FM sound
detector

←——— 6 MHz ———→

Fig. 9-4   continued.

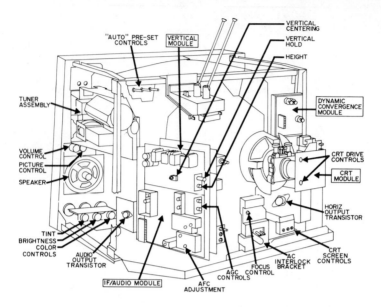

Note: This is only a representative layout, and is not a standard arrangement.

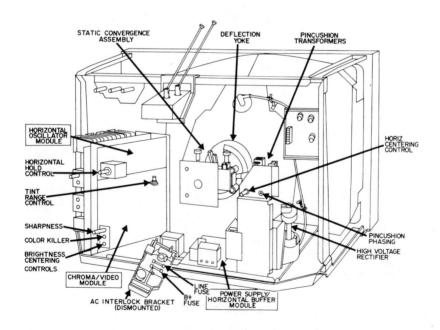

Fig. 9-5   Color-TV chassis with modular construction.

that the CRT module is attached to the color picture tube. Next, the power-supply/horizontal-buffer module is mounted horizontally beneath the CRT modules. All remaining modules, comprising the vertical, horizontal-oscillator, IF/audio, and chroma/video modules, plug into a hinged, moveable interconnect board. The entire assembly, comprising the four modules and the interconnect board, can be swung out or completely removed to provide access either to the modules or to the interior of the receiver. The receiver remains operable although the assembly may be swung out or even dismounted from the chassis. In addition to these plug-in modules, good accessibility is provided to the "off-module" components, including the speaker, tuner assembly, customer controls, auto pre-set controls, high-voltage rectifier, and pincushion transformers.

9-3 Basic Troubleshooting Factors

Color reproduction trouble symptoms do not necessarily point to malfunctions in the chroma section. A weak or no color symptom, with black-and-white reproduction acceptable, could result, for example, from misalignment of the RF tuner. With reference to Figure 9-6, the RF tuned circuits are normally aligned to the color-subcarrier frequency at the top of the

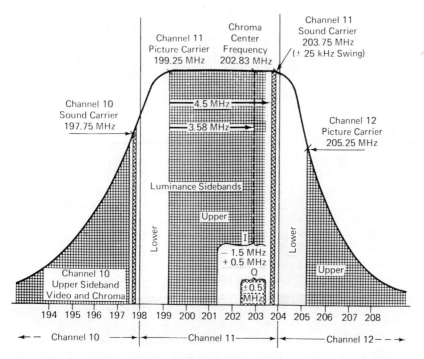

Fig. 9-6   Channel 11 frequency spectrum.

response curve. If a circuit fault causes severe attenuation of the chroma frequencies, leaving the black-and-white (luminance) frequencies at normal amplitude up to approximately the chroma band, the result will be weak or no color reproduction, with black-and-white reproduction acceptable. Accordingly, the diagnostician is advised to make a sweep-frequency check of the RF-tuner frequency response. Similarly, IF section misalignment that attenuates the 3.58-MHz signal can weaken or "kill" color reproduction (see Figure 9-7). In many color receivers, the chroma signal is processed through the video amplifier; poor high-frequency response in this section can result in weak or no color reproduction (see Figure 9-8).

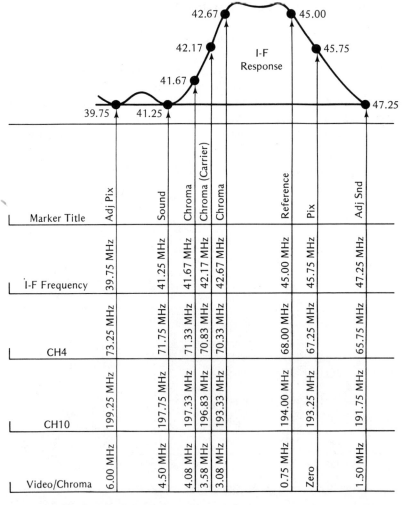

Marker Title	Adj Pix		Sound	Chroma	Chroma (Carrier)	Chroma		Reference	Pix		Adj Snd
I-F Frequency	39.75 MHz		41.25 MHz	41.67 MHz	42.17 MHz	42.67 MHz		45.00 MHz	45.75 MHz		47.25 MHz
CH4	73.25 MHz		71.75 MHz	71.33 MHz	70.83 MHz	70.33 MHz		68.00 MHz	67.25 MHz		65.75 MHz
CH10	199.25 MHz		197.75 MHz	197.33 MHz	196.83 MHz	193.33 MHz		194.00 MHz	193.25 MHz		191.75 MHz
Video/Chroma	6.00 MHz		4.50 MHz	4.08 MHz	3.58 MHz	3.08 MHz		0.75 MHz	Zero		1.50 MHz

Fig. 9-7 Frequency relations along the IF frequency-response curve. (Courtesy, B&K Precision, Division of Dynascan Corp.)

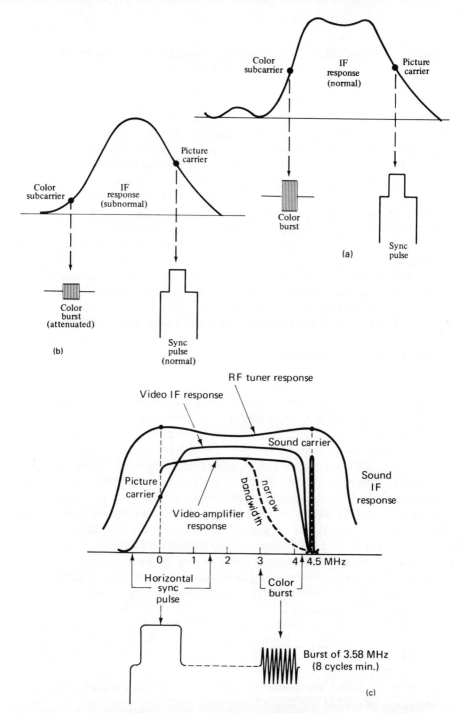

Fig. 9-8 Color-burst processing. (a) Normal amplitude of color burst on response curve; (b) subnormal amplitude on narrow-band response curve; (c) narrow video-amplifier bandwidth attenuates color burst.

The significant frequencies comprising the horizontal sync pulse fall within 1.5 MHz of the picture-carrier frequency. On the other hand, the frequencies comprising the color burst (and chroma signal) fall in the interval from 3.1 MHz to 4.1 MHz from the picture-carrier frequency. It follows that if the video amplifier has deficient high-frequency response, the chroma signal will be attenuated accordingly. Therefore, if an oscilloscope check shows that the chroma-signal component at the video-amplifier output has subnormal amplitude, the repairman should check the video-amplifier frequency response, as explained in the foregoing chapter. With reference to Figure 9-9, a bandpass amplifier, unlike a video amplifier, provides alignment adjustments. L351 and T351 have slug adjustments for contouring the bandpass-amplifier frequency-response curve. Permissible curve tolerances are indicated in (b). Note that a color-killer transistor is included in the bandpass-amplifier network. Its function is to switch off (disable) the bandpass amplifier unless a color-burst signal is present. Confetti (colored snow) is thereby eliminated during black-and-white reception.

9-4 Video Sweep Modulation

Optimum evaluation of color signal-channel frequency response can be made by means of the video-sweep-modulation (VSM) technique as shown in Figure 9-10. This is a specialized type of alignment procedure that shows how the various signal channels work together as a team. It employs an encoded sweep signal. The VSM signal consists of a video-frequency sweep signal that is modulated on the picture-carrier frequency. When the VSM signal is applied to the input terminals of a TV tuner, the signal passes through to the IF amplifier and is then demodulated by the picture detector. In turn, an oscilloscope connected at the output of the picture detector displays the combined RF-IF response of the receiver, as exemplified in Figure 9-10(b). This is a video-frequency sweep signal that has been varied in amplitude according to the response curves of the front end and the IF strip. It has five absorption markers along its envelope, indicating key frequencies in the pattern. Next, if the oscilloscope is connected at the output of the video amplifier, the combined response of the RF, IF, and video amplifiers is displayed. A typical pattern is shown in Figure 9-10(c). Or, if the oscilloscope is connected at the output of the bandpass amplifier, the combined response of the RF, IF, video, and bandpass amplifiers is displayed, as seen in Figure 9-10(d). These patterns are obtained using a low-C probe; if a demodulator probe is employed, the pattern in (b) then appears as shown in (e). The waveform of a VSM test signal is depicted in (f).

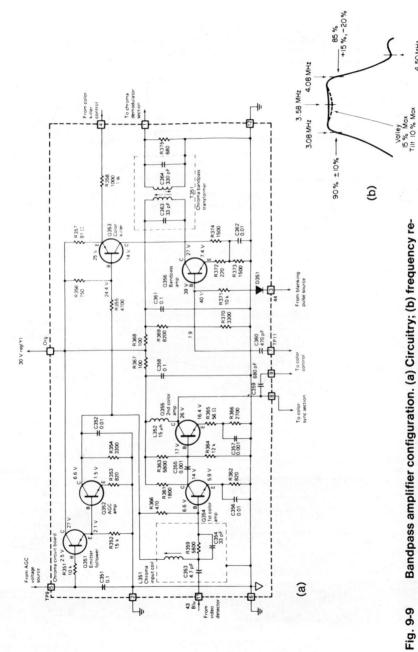

Fig. 9-9   Bandpass amplifier configuration. (a) Circuitry; (b) frequency response curve, with permissible tolerances.

187

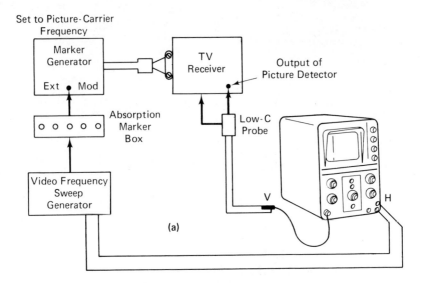

Set to Picture-Carrier Frequency

Marker Generator

Ext • Mod

Absorption Marker Box

Video Frequency Sweep Generator

TV Receiver

Output of Picture Detector

Low-C Probe

V   H

(a)

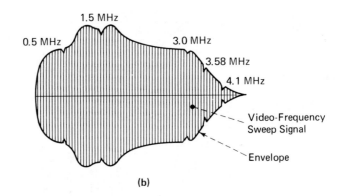

1.5 MHz

0.5 MHz

3.0 MHz

3.58 MHz

4.1 MHz

Video-Frequency Sweep Signal

Envelope

(b)

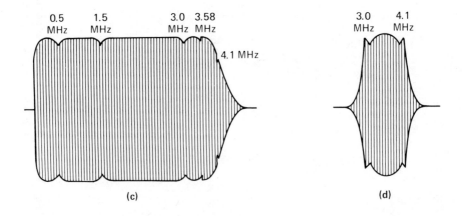

0.5 MHz

1.5 MHz

3.0 MHz

3.58 MHz

4.1 MHz

(c)

3.0 MHz

4.1 MHz

(d)

188

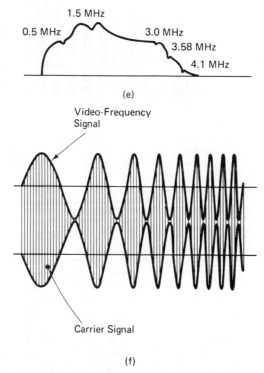

1.5 MHz

0.5 MHz

3.0 MHz

3.58 MHz

4.1 MHz

(e)

Video-Frequency
Signal

Carrier Signal

(f)

Fig. 9-10   **Typical video-sweep-modulation test setup. (a) Equipment connections; (b) representative scope pattern at picture-detector
output; (c) typical pattern at video-amplifier output; (d) pattern
at bandpass-amplifier output; (e) display of (b) when a demodulator probe is used instead of a low-C probe; (f) waveform of a
video-sweep-modulation signal.**

9-5 Specialized Color-TV Test Signals

Diagnosis of chroma trouble symptoms is greatly facilitated by the use
of specialized color test signals. Service technicians generally use a keyed-
rainbow signal for chroma circuit tests, as shown in Figure 9-11(a). This signal consists of groups (bursts) of 3.56-MHz sine-wave voltage; 11 bursts are
followed by a horizontal sync pulse. A keyed-rainbow signal is also called a
sidelock signal, an offset color subcarrier, or a linear phase sweep. Because
the frequency of a rainbow signal is 15,750 Hz less than that of the subcarrier oscillator, its relative phase changes from one horizontal sync pulse to
the next. The color-subcarrier oscillator is automatically referenced to the
first burst following the horizontal sync pulse; this burst has a reference
phase of 0 deg. As indicated in the diagram, the second burst has a relative

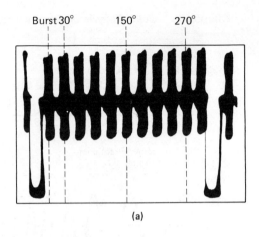

(a)

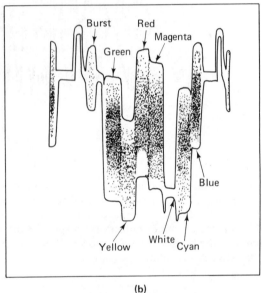

(b)

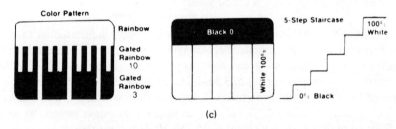

(c)

Fig. 9-11 **Basic color-TV diagnostic waveforms. (a) Standard keyed-rainbow color-bar signal; (b) an NTSC color-bar pattern; (c) combination unkeyed and keyed rainbow pattern with R-Y, B-Y, and G-Y phase indicators and supplementary staircase waveform for linearity checks.**

phase of 30 deg, the sixth burst a relative phase of 150 deg, and the tenth burst a relative phase of 270 deg.

9-6   Transmitter Test Pattern

Transmitter engineers and technicians utilize some form of the National Television Systems Committee (NTSC) color-bar signal, depicted in Figure 9-11(b). This is a comparatively sophisticated type of color test signal that includes chroma and Y signal components for development of fully saturated primary and complementary color-bar displays. A somewhat more complex type of color bar pattern is pictured in Figure 9-12. This is a split-

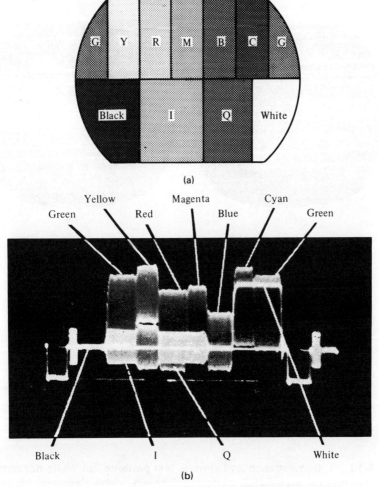

Fig. 9-12   Transmitter color test signal. (a) Complete NTSC color test pattern; (b) display on oscilloscope screen.

field pattern, in which the upper portion of the field displays the primary and complementary colors, and the lower portion of the field displays the transmission primaries I (in-phase) and Q (quadrature phase) signals, along with reference black and white levels. White-dot and crosshatch generators are required in color picture tube convergence procedures. Screen patterns appear as shown in Figure 9-13; the more elaborate service-type color signal generators provide white-dot, crosshatch, keyed-rainbow, and intercarrier-sound outputs.

In addition to the foregoing color test signals, multiburst signals as depicted in Figure 9-14 are often used in diagnostic procedures. A typical multiburst generator was previously pictured in Chapter 2. Observe that a multiburst signal is comparable in some respects to a video sweep signal. It

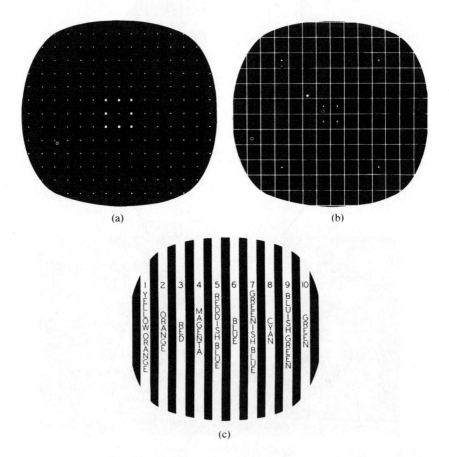

Fig. 9-13   Convergence and chroma test patterns. (a) White-dot pattern; (b) crosshatch pattern; (c) keyed-rainbow pattern; (d) elaborate service-type color signal generator. (Courtesy, Sencore)

(d)

Fig 9-13   continued.

differs, however, in respect to provision of discrete frequency steps from 0.5 MHz to 4.2 MHz, and it has a repetition rate of 15,750 Hz instead of 60 Hz. This distinction is of some technical significance, inasmuch as a linear frequency sweep (video sweep signal) is limited to checks of frequency response only, whereas a multiburst signal with its discrete frequency steps provides checks both of frequency response and of phase response.

If the system under test has uniform response up to 4.3 MHz, the multiburst waveform is displayed on an oscilloscope screen with each of the bursts equal in height and with the tops of the bursts at the "white flag" level. On the other hand, if the system has high-frequency attenuation, the pattern displays successive bursts with decreasing amplitude. Nonlinear phase response results in slowed rise of leading edges in the displayed bursts. A summary of diagnostic procedures using a multiburst test signal is given in Table 9-1. Note that a multiburst generator also finds useful application in servicing of video tape recorders. The color-bar and multiburst signals are used to check the chroma processing stages, and the multiburst signal is utilized to check the luminance stages. Servo circuits are checked with composite sync signals from the generator, and the playback circuits are checked with a tape that has been prerecorded with the multiburst signal.

9-7   Chroma Circuit Diagnosis

Operation of the bandpass amplifier in a color-TV receiver is easily checked with a color-bar signal applied either at the antenna input terminals

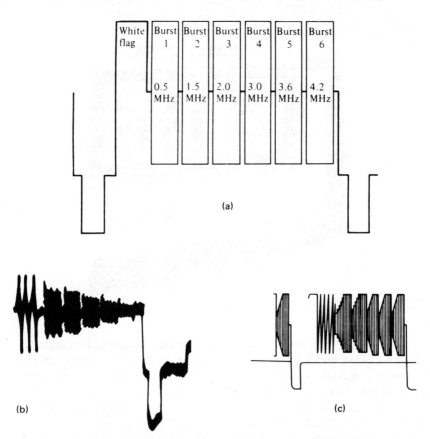

Fig. 9-14   **Multiburst test signal. (a) Generator output waveform; (b) result of high-frequency attenuation; (c) result of nonlinear phase characteristic.**

or at the output of the video amplifier. It is advisable to disable the color killer by turning its threshold to minimum setting during chroma test procedures. If the bandpass amplifier is operating properly, an oscilloscope connected at the output of the amplifier will display a chroma signal waveform, as exemplified in Figure 9-15. In normal operation, the bandpass amplifier rejects the low-frequency Y component from the complete color signal and passes only the higher-frequency chroma component. Note that the normal gain of a bandpass amplifier is not high, and may be as low as unity; the receiver service data will usually specify the input and output waveform amplitudes. Many color receivers include automatic chroma control (ACC) action; in such cases, the repairman should clamp the ACC bias voltage at the value recommended in the receiver service data.

Table 9-1

OVERALL TELEVISION PERFORMANCE TESTS			
All tests performed with VA48 connected to the TV VHF antenna terminals.			
Type of Test	Instructions	Set Should Produce:	Circuits Tested
Sensitivity	Set RF-IF LEVEL control to "NORM"	Snow-free picture Locked in sync Locked in color	RF/IF gain Sync separators Color detectors
Low-level Sensitivity	Reduce RF-IF LEVEL control to .1	Snowy picture Locked in sync Noisy color	AGC Sync separators Color detectors/ color killers
AGC	Increase RF-IF LEVEL control to maximum	No picture tear	AGC
Static Convergence	Switch VIDEO PATTERN to SINGLE DOT	Dot should be white	Yoke magnets
Picture Centering	Switch VIDEO PATTERN to SINGLE CROSS	Cross should be centered	Yoke alignment Centering controls
Dynamic Convergence	Switch VIDEO PATTERN to CROSS HATCH or DOTS	Lines should be straight Lines/dots should be white	Pincushion Convergence coils
Color Demodulators	Switch VIDEO PATTERN to COLOR BARS	Show standard color bars	Color Demodulators
Tint Range	Rotate TV tint control through the entire range	Color should shift at least 3 bars	Tint phase shift
B&W Tracking	Switch VIDEO PATTERN to BAR SWEEP. Release all 5 BAR SWEEP buttons	The 3 remaining bars should have no color information	CRT drive and bias controls
Color Killer	Turn on 3.56 MHz bar	Bar should be grey	Color killer threshold setting
IF/Video Amp Frequency Response	Depress all 5 BAR SWEEP buttons. Reduce brightness and contrast until 1 bar disappears.	3.56 MHz bar should disappear first	3.58 MHz trap
	Continue to reduce brightness/ contrast until second bar disappears	3.02 MHz Bar V should disappear second	IF alignment, video amp
	Increase brightness/contrast to normal level	.188 and .75 MHz bars should not show ringing	IF alignment, video amp
AFT Alignment	Fine tune VHF tuner for good resolution on the 1.51 MHz bar. Turn AFT off and on.	Pattern should not lose detail when AFT is on	AFT alignment
Color Demodulators	Switch VIDEO PATTERN switch to CHROMA BAR SWEEP	Middle bar should be blue	Tint control or tint range
Color Sideband Check	Reduce brightness control until either left or right bar disappears	Both should turn grey or black at the same time	Bandpass amplifier Amplifier
Tuner Test	Feed in signal on each VHF channel	Each should give good picture unless overdriven by strong local signal	VHF tuner

(Courtesy of Sencore)

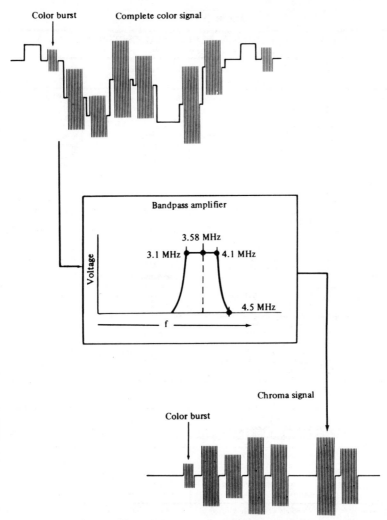

Fig. 9-15   Separation of the chroma signal from the Y signal by the band-pass amplifier.

Consider next the responses of a chroma-demodulator section to a color-bar signal. With reference to Figure 9-16, the bandwidth of the IF amplifier is of concern if the test signal is applied to the antenna input terminals of the receiver. In other words, the keyed-rainbow waveform can become distorted in various degrees in case that the IF amplifier has subnormal bandwidth, as shown in (a). Therefore, the troubleshooter should first check the output waveform from the video detector. If this waveform is normal, he may proceed to check the outputs from the three chroma demod-

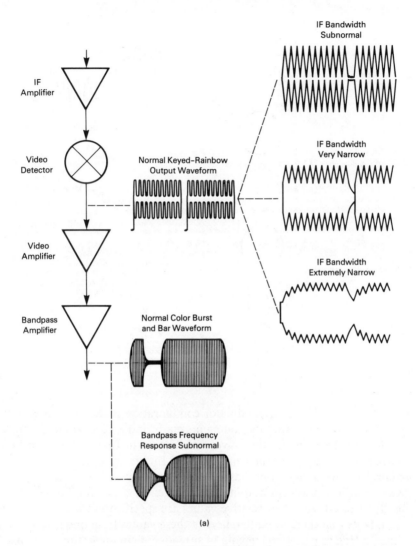

(a)

Fig. 9-16   **Color-bar signal waveform distortion versus circuit bandwidth.
(a) Video-detector output; (b) chroma demodulator output.
(Continued on next page)**

ulators. As exemplified in (b), these waveforms may show a slight amount of baseline curvature in normal operation. However, in the event that excessive baseline curvature occurs, as shown for the G-Y waveform in (b), it is indicated that the demodulator bandwidth is subnormal. Open capacitors in the demodulator circuitry are common culprits.

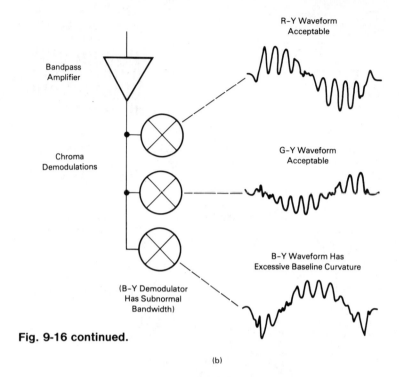

Fig. 9-16 continued.

(b)

A typical chroma-demodulator configuration is shown in Figure 9-17. If the demodulators are functioning normally and a keyed-rainbow signal is applied to the receiver, the waveforms shown in Figure 9-18 will be displayed at the outputs of the demodulators. In this example, the vertical-gain control of the oscilloscope has been adjusted in each case to display the waveform at a uniform amplitude. In practice, these amplitudes are normally unequal, and their relative values are specified in the receiver service data. Note that there are differences in these values from one receiver to another, owing to variations in gain of subsequent circuit sections and also because of differences in efficiencies of phosphors used in various color picture tubes. As a practical note, the first pulse or the last pulse in the waveforms of Figure 9-18 may be obscured, owing to the action of the horizontal blanking pulse in the receiver circuitry. When this difficulty is encountered, the technician should disable the blanker output with a bypass capacitor. Note also that if the horizontal-hold control is turned somewhat to the left or to the right, the displayed waveform will move horizontally on the screen accordingly. In turn, the first pulse or the last pulse can be brought into view.

An essential consideration in analysis of chroma-demodulator waveforms is their relative-phase relations. As an illustration, with reference to

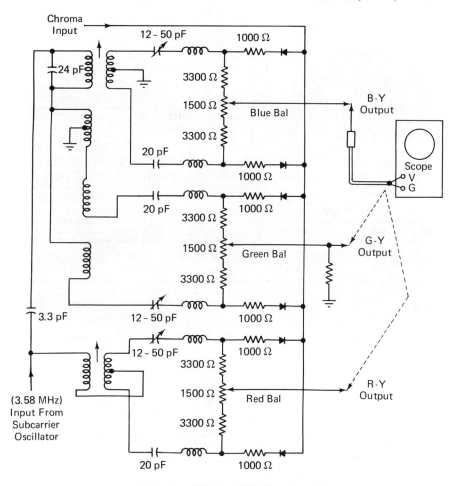

Fig. 9-17   Chroma demodulation of R-Y, B-Y, and G-Y signals.

Figure 9-18, normal null points are shown. That is, the R-Y waveform nulls at the sixth position, the B-Y waveform nulls at the third and ninth positions, and the G-Y waveform nulls at the first and seventh positions. When incorrect null points are displayed, the repairman concludes that the subcarrier injection phases are incorrect. Refer to Figure 9-17; the subcarrier phase for the B-Y demodulator is adjusted by the 12-50 pF trimmer capacitor in the secondary output lead; similar trimmer capacitors are provided in the G-Y and in the R-Y sections. In addition, a trimming slug is provided in the R-Y coupling transformer. When phase errors are caused by component or device defects, it will be found impossible to bring the associated waveform into correct phase and with correct relative amplitude. In this situation, the repairman checks the associated components and devices.

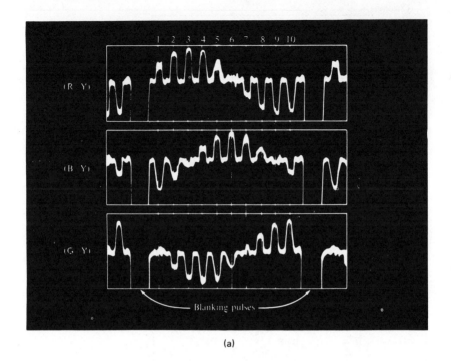

(a)

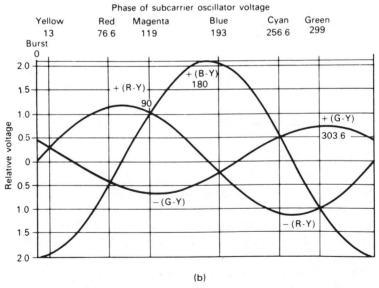

(b)

Fig. 9-18   Example of normal R-Y, B-Y, and G-Y waveforms. (a) Chroma-
              demodulator output waveforms; (b) relative waveform ampli-
              tudes for a typical color receiver. (Courtesy, Sencore)

9-8 Vectorscope Techniques

Diagnostic procedures are often facilitated by vectorscope checks, as depicted in Figure 9-19. In this example, the output from the R-Y demodulator is applied to the vertical-input terminals of an oscilloscope, and the output from the B-Y demodulator is applied to the horizontal-input terminals. In turn, a specialized type of Lissajous figure called a vectorgram is displayed on the oscilloscope screen, as exemplified in Figure 9-20. Basically, each "petal" in a vectorgram is a chroma-phase vector or phasor. Each phasor is 30 deg from its preceding and from its succeeding phasor. Each phasor is associated with a particular hue in the color image. The R-Y and B-Y signals will normally produce a circular vectorgram when the gains of the vertical and horizontal channels in the oscilloscope are equalized. If a circular pattern is not displayed, it is indicated that the subcarrier-injection phases into the R-Y and B-Y demodulators have a phase difference less than or greater than 90 deg. In practice, 10 "petals" are normally displayed in a vectorgram. The phasors that would otherwise occupy the 11th and the 12th positions are blanked out during the horizontal-retrace interval.

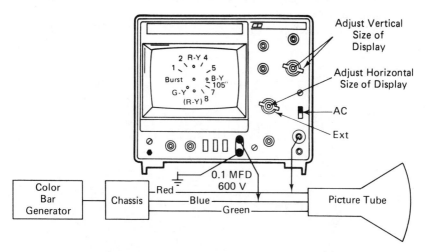

Fig. 9-19 **Test setup for vectorgram display. (Courtesy, B&K Precision, Division of Dynascan Corp.)**

Observe that the "petals" shown in Figure 9-20 do not have straight sides and flat tops, as in theory. These departures from ideal waveshape result from the fact that the chroma demodulator bandwidth is somewhat limited (0.5 MHz) and the phase characteristics of the demodulator circuits vary to some extent as a function of signal amplitude. Restricted demodulator bandwidth has two basic effects on vectorgram waveshape. It rounds off the tops of the "petals," much as sync pulses acquire rounded tops in passage through narrow-band circuitry. Another effect of limited bandwidth in the chroma-demodulator circuitry is the development of an open area at the center of the vectorgram, as seen in Figure 9-20. In other words, limited bandwidth introduces curvature into the base line of a demodulator output waveform. Baseline curvatures result in development of an open area in the center of the pattern. An excessively large open area points to subnormal demodulator bandwidth.

If the R-Y and B-Y nulls are incorrect in the demodulator output waveforms, an elliptical vectorgram is displayed. The third petal in a vectorgram normally falls at the top of the pattern, as exemplified in Figure 9-20. This placement will change with the setting of the color-phasing (tint) control in the receiver. As the tint-control setting is varied, the vectorgram rotates correspondingly on the oscilloscope screen. As the color-intensity (color) control is turned, the amplitude of the vectorgram changes accordingly. If the color control is advanced to maximum, it often happens that the chroma-demodulator section becomes overloaded, with a resulting "flat" in the contour of the vectorgram pattern. However, no evidence of overloading should appear at the normal setting of the color control—otherwise, it is indicated that there is a defect in the associated chroma-demodulator channel.

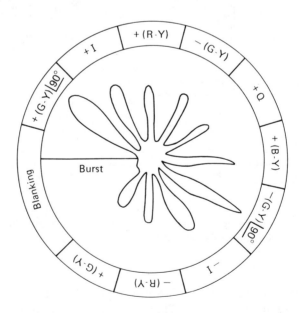

Fig. 9-20   Development of a vectorgram.

Phasor placement and the number of "petals" that are displayed in a vectorgram can be affected by the setting of the automatic tint control (ATC) that is provided in some receivers. With reference to Figure 9-21, phasors 1 and 3 are moved in toward the phasor 2 position as the ATC switch is turned. At the full ATC setting, the first and third phasors merge with the second phasor. Thus, this sequence of patterns serves as a quick check of ATC action. Note that the vectorgrams that have been discussed are those developed by R-Y and B-Y signals. Some receivers utilize X and Z demodulation, with the result that the associated demodulator vectorgrams have relevant characteristics. In turn, the repairman should consult the service data for the particular receiver to determine the specified vectorgram pattern.

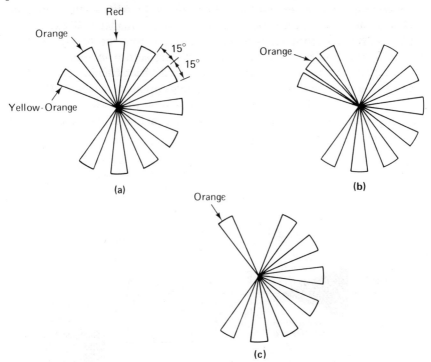

Fig. 9-21 **Idealized vectorgrams showing ATC action. (a) ATC switch off; (b) partial ATC; (c) full ATC.**

9-9 Burst Waveform Checks

Burst waveforms can be checked to best advantage with a triggered-sweep oscilloscope. With reference to Figure 9-22, this area of the color receiver comprises a burst amplifier, phase-comparator and AFC circuitry, and the 3.58-MHz subcarrier oscillator. The burst waveform should be checked first at the input to the burst amplifier, as shown in (b). In this example, the 3.58-MHz crystal is shock-excited by the color-burst waveform, and the phase-comparator/AFC section functions to control the capacitance of a varactor diode as required to maintain color sync lock. If the input burst waveform has normal amplitude and waveshape, the repairman proceeds to check the output from the buffer transistor. This is normally a sine wave of specified amplitude. Note that the tint control in the AFC section functions to change the phase of the subcarrier voltage in accordance with the control setting. The burst amplifier is gated by a pulse from the flyback section. Normal gating and burst-output waveforms are shown in Figure 9-23, as displayed on the screen of a dual-trace triggered-sweep oscilloscope. Timing of the gating pulse relative to the burst depends upon the setting of the horizontal-hold control. Thus, if the timing is incorrect when the hold control is set to the midpoint of its range, the repairman concludes that there is a component or device defect in the gating circuitry.

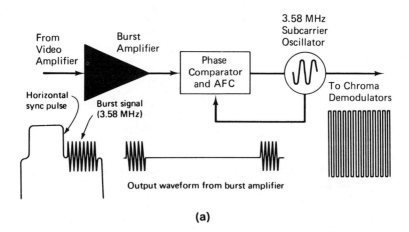

(a)

Fig. 9-22   Burst amplifier checks. (a) Plan of burst-amplifier section; (b) oscilloscope check of burst-amplifier circuitry; (c) expanded display of the color burst.

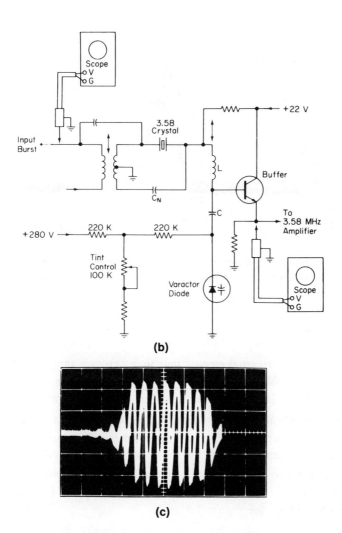

(b)

(c)

Fig. 9-22   **continued.**

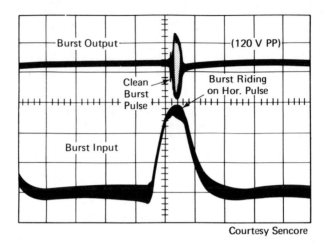

Courtesy Sencore

Fig. 9-23   Burst-gating pulse and burst output waveforms as displayed by a dual-trace triggered-sweep oscilloscope. (Courtesy, Sencore)

Review Questions

1. Name the four principal signals that flow through the tuner and IF amplifier in a color-TV receiver.

2. Where is the Y signal separated from the complete color signal?

3. Where is the chroma signal separated from the complete color signal?

4. Do color reproduction trouble symptoms necessarily point to malfunctions in the chroma section?

5. What are the two most important specialized color-TV test signals?

6. Identify the R-Y, B-Y, and G-Y signals with respect to blue, red, and green hues (Hint: See Figure 9-1).

7. If a chroma demodulator has subnormal bandwidth, how is the waveform of a keyed-rainbow signal affected?

8. How are chroma-demodulator phases checked?

9. Explain how an oscilloscope is connected into the chroma-output circuitry for display of a vectorgram.

10. Give an example of a dual-trace oscilloscope application in chroma-circuit testing.

Chapter 10

Color-TV Set-Up Procedures and Integrated Circuit Notes

10-1 General Considerations

Color-TV set-up procedures are concerned with maintenance adjustments as follows:

1. Adjustment of the pre-set fine-tuning trimmers
2. Adjustment of the AGC level control
3. Adjustment of the picture-peaking control (if present)
4. Adjustment of the noise-gate control
5. Adjustment of the vertical-linearity control
6. Adjustment of the vertical-height control
7. Adjustment of the high-voltage and focus-voltage values
8. Adjustment of the horizontal-hold control
9. Adjustment of the color picture tube gun controls
10. Adjustment of the convergence controls

Two principal types of color picture tubes are in general use. These are described as the shadow-mask design and the aperture-grille design. All shadow-mask tubes have comparatively elaborate convergence circuitry. On the other hand, most aperture-grille tubes have comparatively simple convergence circuitry. One design has unadjustable (fixed) convergence facilities, so that the technician is never concerned with convergence adjustments; the tube has yokes bonded to its neck.

Set-up procedures are related in some respects to the type of chroma circuitry used in a receiver. Thus, the signal section may include only the cathodes of the color picture tube, as depicted in Figure 10-1. On the other hand, the signal section may include both the cathodes and the grids of the picture tube, as shown in Figure 10-2. When the cathodes alone are driven, the grids operate at fixed DC bias voltages. However, when both the cathodes and the grids are driven, the AC grid voltages cause the dynamic range adjustments to be somewhat more involved. Figure 10-3 shows the terminal points and neck components on a conventional color picture tube. There are two heater terminals, three cathode terminals, three control-grid terminals, three screen-grid terminals, a high-voltage terminal, and a focus-grid terminal brought out from the picture tube. External component circuit terminals include four deflection-yoke leads and 12 convergence-coil leads. DC voltage is applied to all the picture-tube terminals, with the exception of the heater, which operates on AC voltage.

The deflection-yoke windings and the convergence-yoke windings are driven by nonsinusoidal AC voltages. Convergence circuitry is comparatively complex and employs inductors, capacitors, resistors, and semiconductor diodes. Capacitors are usually suspected first in case of malfunction, and diodes are the next most likely devices to develop defects.

10-2 Convergence Procedures

A color picture tube is converged with the aid of a white-dot or cross-hatch pattern. Dots at the center of the screen are brought into convergence by adjustment of the static-convergence controls. In most cases, the dots elsewhere on the screen will be out of convergence. Dynamic convergence adjustments are made to obtain a properly converged white-dot or cross-hatch pattern over the entire screen area. As dynamic-convergence adjustments are being made, convergence at center screen tends to become disturbed. As misconvergence becomes evident at center screen, the technician touches up adjustment of the static controls, as required. Figure 10-4 depicts a typical dynamic convergence-control board layout. These controls are adjusted in sequence, as tabulated in Table 10-1, to obtain progressively improved convergence toward the edges of the screen. In most cases, the screen convergence will be satisfactory after completion of the fourteenth adjustment. However, if the initial convergence is very poor, it may be necessary to repeat part or all of the dynamic-convergence adjustments, owing to control interactions.

Some shadow-mask color picture tubes require blue horizontal shaping-coil adjustment, wide blue-field adjustment, and dynamic pincushion adjustments. When a blue horizontal shaping coil is provided, a test point is available on the dynamic-convergence board for connection of an oscilloscope. The slug in the shaping coil is adjusted to obtain the waveform depicted in Figure 10-5(f). Unless this waveform is properly shaped, optimum

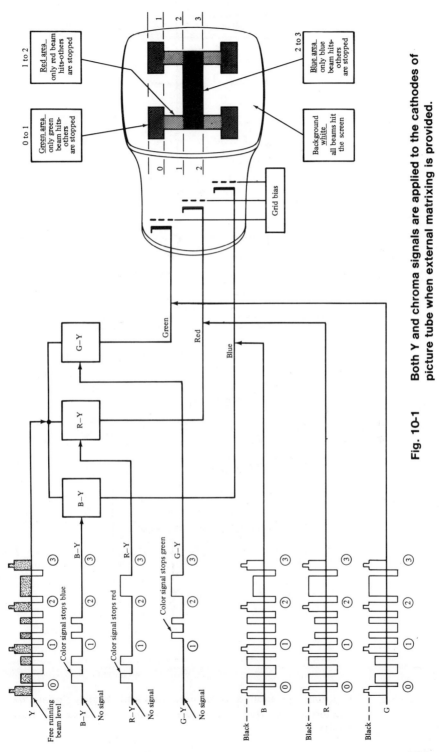

Fig. 10-1   Both Y and chroma signals are applied to the cathodes of picture tube when external matrixing is provided.

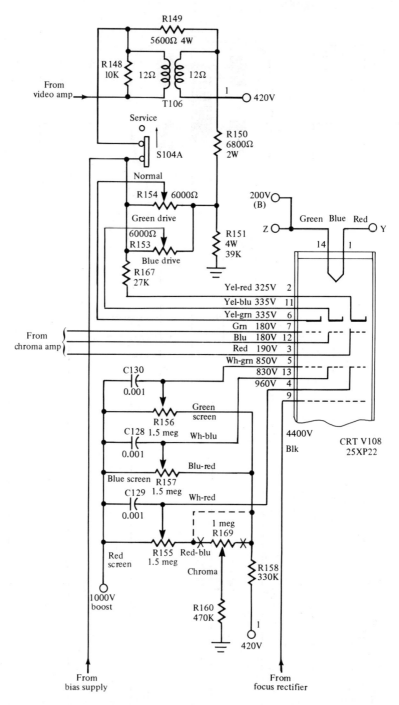

Fig. 10-2 Y signals are applied to the cathodes and chroma signals are applied to the grids of a picture tube that operates also as a matrix.

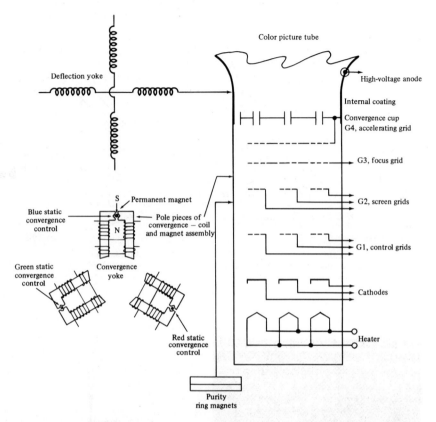

Fig. 10-3 **Terminal points and components on a conventional color picture tube.**

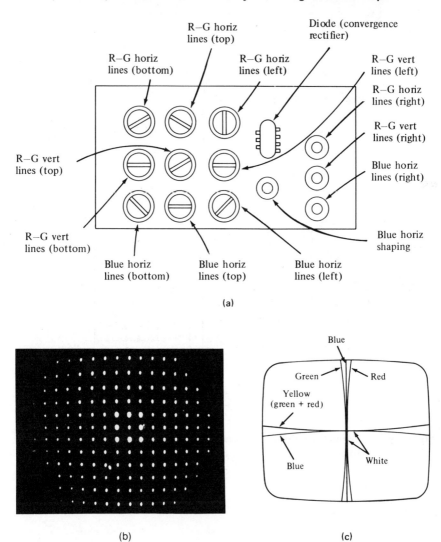

Fig. 10-4 Dynamic convergence controls for a conventional color picture tube. (a) Control board layout; (b) dot pattern displayed for good convergence; (c) good static convergence, but poor dynamic convergence.

Table 10-1   Convergence adjustments

Step	Control	Use to converge (or straighten)	Remarks
1.			Perform center dot convergence using convergence magnets. (See Fig. 8-5 (a))
2.	R–G vertical lines, top	Red and green vertical bars at top of screen	Touch up both controls for best convergence from top to bottom along vertical center line (Fig. 8-5 (b))
3.	R–G vertical lines, bottom	Red and green vertical bars at bottom of screen	
4.	R–G horizontal lines, top	Red and green horizontal bars at top of screen	Touch up both controls for best convergence of horizontal bars along vertical center line (Fig. 8-5 (b))
5.	R–G horizontal lines, bottom	Red and green horizontal bars at bottom of screen	
6.	Blue horizontal lines, top	Blue horizontal bars at top of screen	Touch up both controls for best convergence of horizontal bars along vertical center line (Fig. 8-5 (c))
7.	Blue horizontal lines, bottom	Blue horizontal bars at bottom of screen	
8.			Perform center dot static convergence (Fig. 8-5 (a))
9.	Blue horizontal lines, right	Blue horizontal bars at right side of screen	Touch up both controls for best convergence along horizontal center line (Fig. 8-5 (d))
10.	Blue horizontal lines, left	Blue horizontal bars at left side of screen	
11.	R–G vertical lines, right	Red and green vertical bars at right side of screen	(Fig. 8-5 (e))
12.	R–G horizontal lines, right	Red and green horizontal bars at right side of screen	Use control to converge blue bar with red and green bars on right side of screen (Fig. 8-5 (e))
13.	R–G vertical lines, left	Red and green vertical bars at left side of screen	
14.	R–G horizontal lines, left	Red and green horizontal bars at left side of screen	Use control to converge blue bar with red and green bars at left side of screen (Fig. 8-5 (e))

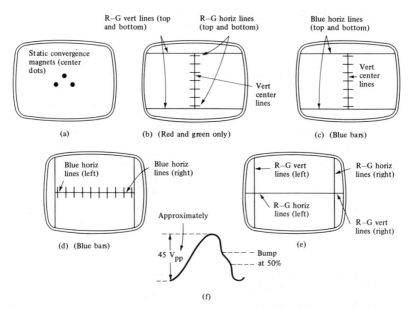

Fig. 10-5 Convergence patterns and terminology. (a)–(e) Static and dynamic convergence indications; (f) shaping-coil waveform.

dynamic convergence cannot be obtained because the blue line will tend to be curved instead of straight. If a wide blue-field adjustment is provided, an adjusting screw will be observed on the bottom of the yoke assembly. This adjustment is made to bring the vertical height of the blue field exactly the same as the height of the red and green fields. Misadjustment of the blue-field height will impair dynamic convergence. Dynamic pincushion adjustments are commonly provided for large-screen shadow-mask picture tubes (see Figure 10-6). These adjustments are made at the factory and seldom require attention. However, if the raster edges appear curved instead of straight, the pincushion adjustments should be touched up as required (topic is detailed subsequently).

10-3 Dynamic Convergence Circuit Action

Troubleshooting the dynamic-convergence circuitry requires an understanding of the circuit actions that are associated with various trouble symptoms. As noted above, edge-screen convergence is effected by horizontal and vertical electromagnets mounted over the electron guns on the picture-tube neck. Current waveforms in step with the horizontal- and vertical-sweep voltages are passed through the horizontal and vertical dynamic-convergence coils (Figure 10-7). These electromagnetic fields correct

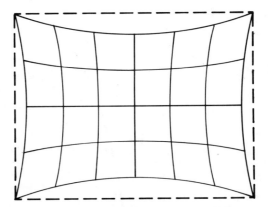

Fig. 10-6   Curved vertical and horizontal lines caused by pincushion distortion.

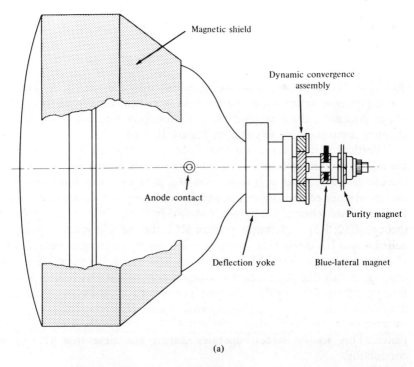

(a)

Fig. 10-7   Dynamic convergence assembly. (a) Location on picture-tube neck; (b) basic current waveform is a parabola. (Continued on next page)

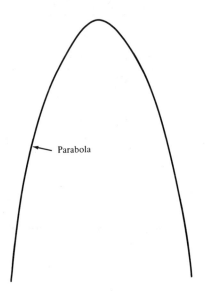

Parabola

Fig. 10-7   continued.   (b)

the beam directions as they are being deflected by the yoke field. Dynamic-convergence waveforms necessarily have a critical amplitude, shape, and phase. Basically, the corrective current waveform that is required has the shape of a parabola, as depicted in Figure 10-7(b).

Vertical parabolic current waveforms are obtained by processing the vertical sawtooth deflection voltage. Partial integration of this sawtooth waveform produces an approximation of a parabolic waveform. Integrated and differentiated versions of a sawtooth waveform are shown in Figure 10-8. A sectional schematic diagram is shown in Figure 10-9. Current flowing through C52, R51, differential resistor R52, the red and green convergence coils L4 and L5, diode D53, and to the B+ supply converges the upper half of the raster. Capacitor C52 and resistors R54 and R55 operate in a wave-shaping circuit that produces the required convergence waveform. Current flowing through resistor R54, differential resistor R53, the convergence coils, amplitude resistor R58, shaping-network diodes D51 and D52 and their associated capacitor, and resistor R56 with C51 converges the lower half of the raster. This second circuit operates during the time that D53 is not conducting.

The amplitude controls in Figure 10-9, R54 and R58, control the amount of correction in convergence of the vertical lines, whereas the differential controls R52 and R53 govern the amount of correction in vertical

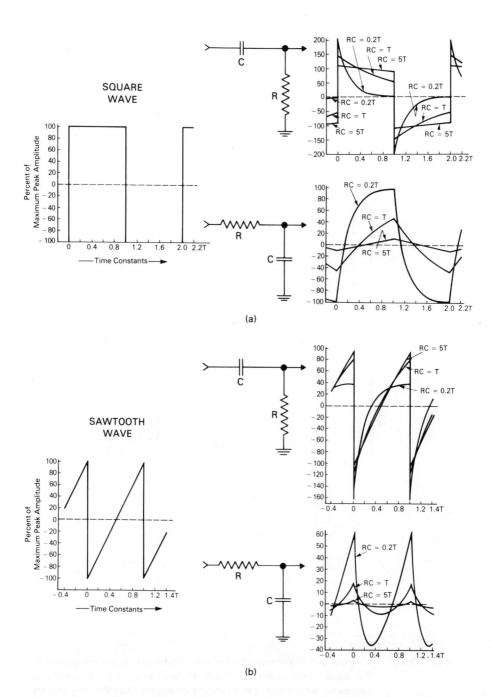

Fig. 10-8   Integration and differentiation of basic complex waveforms.

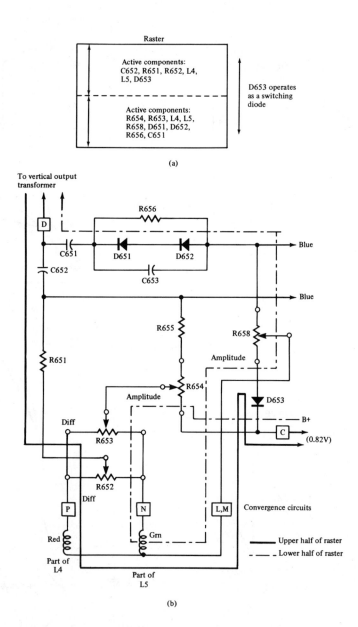

Fig. 10-9 Vertical parabolic waveforms are produced for convergence of the upper and lower portions of the raster by integrating a sawtooth waveform. (a) Portions of raster that are separately converged; (b) network arrangement.

convergence of the horizontal lines at the top and bottom of the raster. Figure 10-10 shows the basic convergence circuit for converging the blue horizontal lines vertically. Controls R59 and R60 effect convergence at the top and bottom halves of the raster. This circuit is energized from the same source that is utilized by the red and green convergence circuits. However, its output is supplied to L6, the convergence coil mounted over the blue gun.

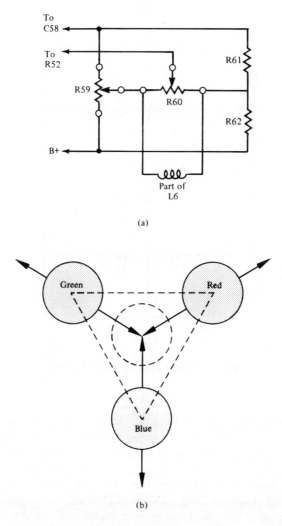

(a)

(b)

Fig. 10-10   **Basic convergence circuit for vertical convergence of the blue horizontal lines. (a) Configuration; (b) dot motions produced by convergence fields.**

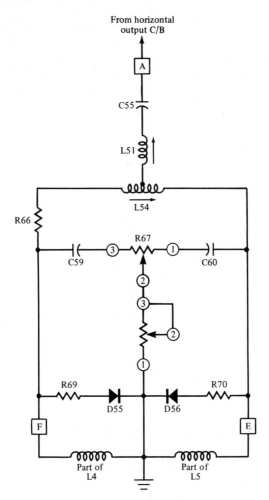

Fig. 10-11 **Plan of horizontal-convergence circuitry.**

Next, consider the plan of the horizontal convergence circuitry. Figure 10-11 shows a basic schematic diagram of this section. Flyback pulses are fed to coil L51, controls R67 and R68, and capacitors C59 and C60 to generate sawtooth waveforms that are applied to the red and green convergence coils. In turn, integrating action produces parabolic waveforms through the coils. Note that clamping diodes D55 and D56 and the associated resistors rectify a portion of the parabolic current waveform, thereby adding a DC component to the convergence waveform. This DC component is required to ensure that the current through the convergence coils is zero as the scanning beam passes through the center of the screen. Coil L54 and control R67 provide a difference-current flow through the red and green convergence coils. This differential current flow corrects symmetrical errors in horizontal-line convergence on the left and right sides of the screen.

Figure 10-12 shows a basic configuration for the blue horizontal convergence circuits, which operate in basically the same manner as the green and red horizontal convergence circuits previously described. However, an additional waveshaping network comprising coil L53, capacitor C57, and resistor R63 is included. This waveshape adds a small amount of second-harmonic sine-wave current to the blue-convergence coil current. Thereby, the blue horizontal convergence waveform is optimized.

A complete circuit-board configuration is shown in Figure 10-13. This assembly employs the partial circuit diagrams, with the same identifications, that are discussed above. Note that 13 maintenance controls are provided, which are adjusted in color picture-tube setup procedures. Nine of these are

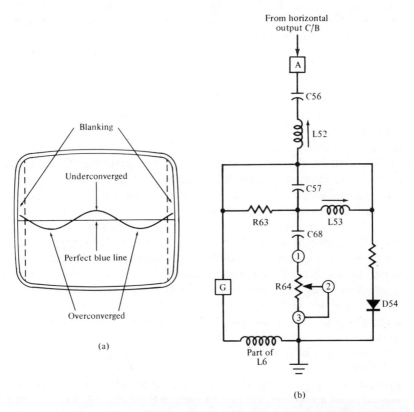

Fig. 10-12   **Effect of second-harmonic voltage in blue horizontal convergence. (a) Underconverged, overconverged, and perfect blue-line displays; (b) basic circuitry for blue horizontal-convergence section.**

resistive controls; four are inductive controls. There is considerable inter-action among the convergence controls because the fields from the three pole pieces affect the directions of all three electron beams to a greater or lesser extent. In practice, this interaction results in a comparatively involved convergence set-up procedure. Skill and speed in the convergence of a shadow-mask picture tube are acquired by a combination of study and experience.

In the example of Figure 10-13, six other maintenance controls are mounted on the convergence panel assembly. However, these are not in-cluded in the convergence circuitry. The dot control operates in conjunction with the horizontal sweep circuit to generate white-dot pulses that are uti-lized in convergence checks. Note that only a minority of color receivers in-clude built-in dot generators. The height control is part of the vertical-deflection system; the AGC control is part of the gain-control system; the color-killer is part of the chroma system. The video peaking control provides an adjustable load resistance so that the high-frequency response in the pic-ture channel can be trimmed to optimize weak-signal or strong-signal reception.

10-4 Aperture-Grille Color Picture Tubes

Convergence procedures are considerably simplified in the case of most designs of aperture-grille picture tubes and are somewhat simplified even with the elaborate designs. The integral-yokes construction, while compara-tively costly, practically eliminates convergence adjustments. With reference to Figure 10-14, the basic components of the aperture-grille color picture tube are the electron-gun assembly, the aperture grille, and the phosphor-stripe screen. Observe that the three electron guns are located in-line hori-zontally; for this reason, the aperture-grille picture tube is also called the in-line tube. All three electron beams pass through the same slot in the grille, but follow different angles. In turn, the beam from the red gun strikes the red phosphor stripe, the beam from the green gun strikes the green phosphor stripe, and the beam from the blue gun strikes the blue phosphor stripe. This action is normally the same for any slot at any point on the screen.

An aperture-grille picture tube operates from the same signal wave-forms as the shadow-mask tube. As an illustration, if the red and green guns were energized, and the blue gun cut off, a yellow field would be displayed with either type of picture tube. Again, if all three guns were energized, a white field would be displayed with either type of picture tube. On the other hand, the convergence waveforms and adjustments for the two types of color picture tubes are quite different. As seen in Figure 10-14, an aperture-grille picture tube employs three in-line cathodes. Emitted electrons pass through small holes in the control grid G1. Next, the electrons are speeded up by the screen-grid or accelerating electrode, G2. In turn, the electrons pass through holes in the electrode and proceed at high speed into the focus-electrode re-

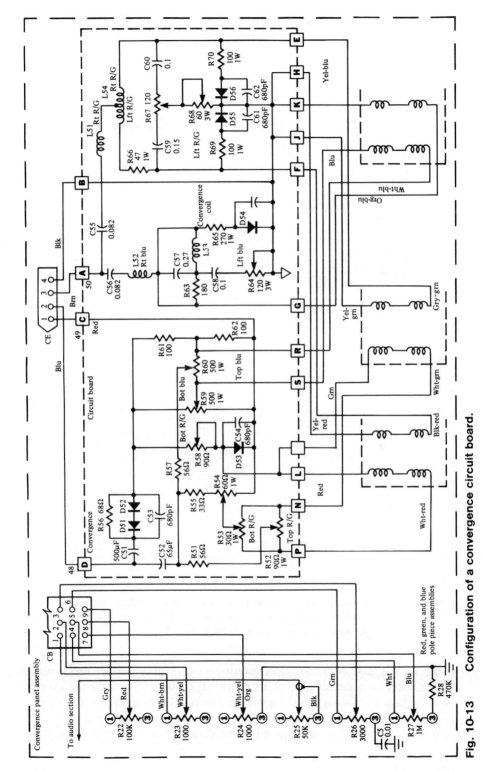

Fig. 10-13 Configuration of a convergence circuit board.

223

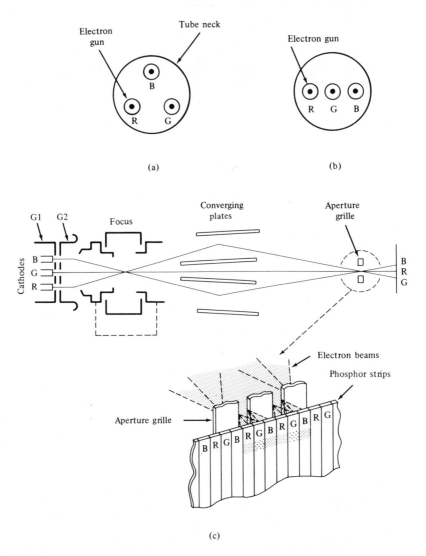

Fig. 10-14   Arrangement of an aperture-grille color picture tube. (a) Conventional delta gun arrangement; (b) in-line gun arrangement; (c) functional features of the in-line tube.

gion. This is essentially an electrostatic-lens assembly, which brings the electron beams together at a point on the aperture grille. Only the green electron beam proceeds in a straight line. The red and blue beams diverge to the left and right in accordance with their original trajectories. Focusing action also has the effect of minimizing the diameter of each electron beam.

These three beams are attracted to the converging plates, which operate typically at 19,000 volts. Thus, a second electron-lens arrangement functions to bring the beams to precise focus on the aperture grille.

Field purity is obtained by proper adjustment of the purity magnet and by correct positioning of the deflection yoke. With reference to Figure 10-15, the purity magnet is adjusted to obtain optimum purity at the center of the screen. Then the deflection yoke is moved to a position that provides maximum purity out to the screen edges. A green field is ordinarily used in this procedure. The purity magnet shifts all three beams by the same amount at all points on the screen. On the other hand, the deflection-yoke position shifts the beams much more at the screen edges than at the center of the screen. Another purity control utilized on the aperture-grille tube is called a neck-twist coil. It is mounted on the rear of the tube neck. This adjustment affects the red and green beams as depicted in Figure 10-16. Basically, this arrangement consists of the same purity-magnet design that is used with a shadow-mask type of tube. Adjustment of the neck-twist coil is usually made with respect to a red-field display.

Convergence at the screen edges requires the addition of a parabolic voltage waveform to the converging plates in Figure 10-14. That is, a parabolic waveform (Figure 10-17) is superimposed on the DC focusing voltage. This waveform can be tilted one way or the other by means of a sawtooth voltage from the horizontal dynamic control. Tilt adjustment is provided to compensate for manufacturing tolerances on replacement picture tubes. The final convergence adjustment is called a vertical static control. This is a DC electromagnet arrangement that operates as a static convergence control (see Figure 10-18). The static control is mounted so that the vertical beam directions are affected. It is the only vertical convergence control provided for the aperture-grille type of picture tube, and it is generally adjusted first in the convergence procedure.

Observe in Figure 10-18 that the cathodes are driven by the outputs from the color video amplifiers. In other words, the aperture-grille tube is not used as an RGB matrix. All matrixing operations are accomplished in the receiver circuitry. Neon lamps are provided in the cathode circuits to protect the picture tube against possible excessive cathode potentials. R1 and C1 provide a compensated attenuating pad, which operates as part of the video-amplifier system to provide correct relative color-signal levels. As noted above, the readjusted chroma values that energize the chroma demodulators must be changed into unadjusted chroma values before application to the color picture tube. Otherwise, the relative color intensities would be in error, and the blue hues, in particular, would be too weak. Blanking pulses are applied to the control grid of the picture tube to make the retrace lines invisible.

From a practical viewpoint, the in-line tube is much the same as the trinitron tube, except that no convergence adjustments are required. An in-line picture tube of this design has factory-sealed purity and convergence

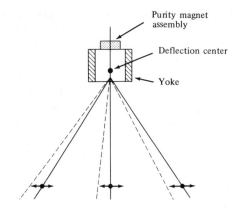

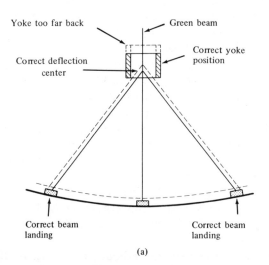

(a)

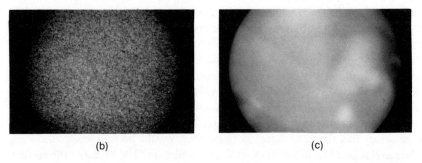

(b)   (c)

Fig. 10-15   **Correct field purity requires proper positioning of the deflection yoke. (a) Principle of purity adjustment; (b) good field purity; (c) poor field purity.**

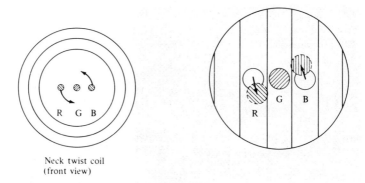

Neck twist coil
(front view)

Fig. 10-16   Principle of neck-twist coil.

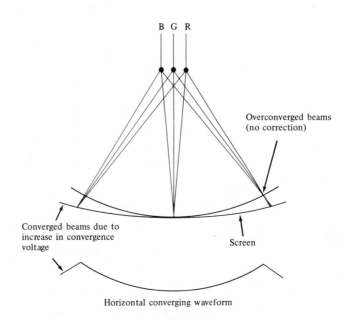

Fig. 10-17   Electron beams are over-converged at screen edges unless a parabolic correction voltage is utilized.

components and requires no adjustment. The deflection yoke is permanently mounted on the neck of the tube. In turn, when the picture tube is replaced, the yoke, purity, and convergence components are also replaced.

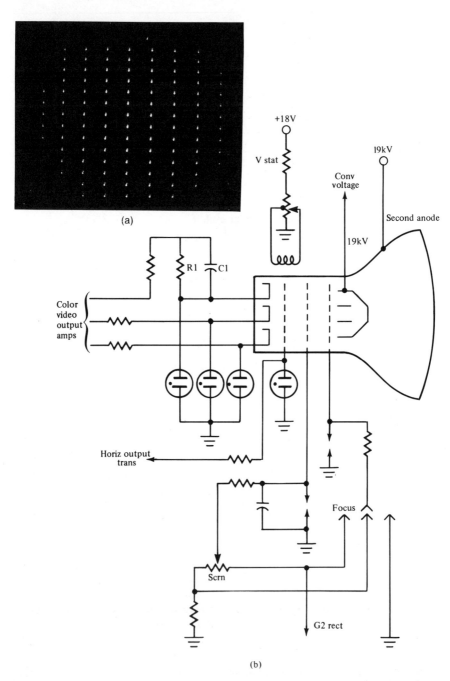

(a)

(b)

Fig. 10-18 **Vertical static control is an electromagnetic field adjustment. (a) Example of misadjustment; (b) configuration.**

10-5   Modules and Integrated Circuits

Integrated circuits are widely used with unipolar and bipolar transistors in TV circuitry. Various types of integrated circuits (IC's) are depicted in Figure 10-19. In many receiver designs, IC's and other devices and components are mounted on modules. Modules are plug-in circuit-board units, such as those illustrated in Figure 10-20. This design tends to simplify diagnostic and repair procedure because a module that has a suspected defect can be replaced quickly with a new (or reconditioned) module, and the receiver can thereby be restored to normal operating condition with a minimum number of tests. In turn, a defective module can be repaired at any

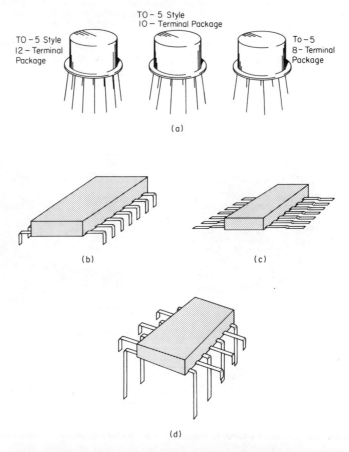

Fig. 10-19   **Integrated circuit packages. (a) TO-5 style package; (b) flat pack with through-board terminals; (c) flat pack with surface-mounting terminals; (d) flat pack with staggered leads; (e) symbol.**

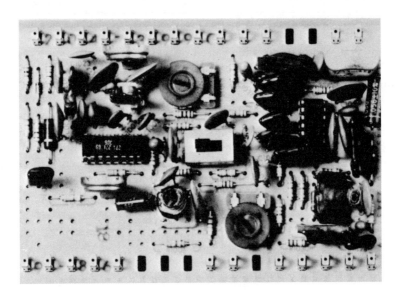

(a)

(b)

(c)

Fig. 10-20   Examples of color-television modules. (a) Typical chroma module (RCA); (b) another module design (Zenith); (c) a widely used horizontal-oscillator module (RCA).

time. In the event that a module is seriously damaged, the repairman may choose to discard it. A color receiver that has modular construction is seldom taken to a shop for repair—all servicing procedures are ordinarily completed in the customer's home.

A typical color-TV receiver employs nine modules to perform the func-

tions of IF amplification and automatic frequency control, sound demodulation, video amplification and picture-tube driving, chroma demodulation,
vertical deflection, and horizontal deflection. A power-supply module may
also be provided in some designs. Note that the functional classification of a
module may be complete or partial. As an illustration, a module may have a
complete video-amplifier function and partial sync function, such as a sync-
separator stage. Again, a module may have a partial function completed by
conventionally mounted chassis components. For instance, an audio-amplifier module may have to be supplemented by chassis-mounted audio-output
components.

A block diagram for a modular receiver, with the functions of the various modules noted, is shown in Figure 10-21. The tuner, as would be ex-
pected, is a chassis-mounted component. It is coupled by a 50-ohm line to
the IF module, as depicted in Figure 10-22. This coupling method simplifies
servicing procedures, because it makes the alignment of L1 independent of
the alignment of L2, L3, L4, T1, and T2. That is, if the tuner is replaced,
realignment of the IF circuits on the module is not required. Or, if the IF
module is replaced, realignment of the tuner output coil L1 is not required.
A typical IF module employs two integrated circuits and two transistors.
When IF trouble symptoms occur, it is sometimes possible to pinpoint the
faulty device or component promptly and to repair the module without
delay. As an illustration, if either of the transistors happens to fail, or if there
is some visible defect, an easy and rapid repair is often possible. However, if
the trouble cannot be localized within a few minutes, the repairman should
simply replace the module.

(a)

**Fig. 10-21   Modular chassis arrangement. (a) Rear view of classical
CTC49 chassis (RCA); (b) block diagram of chassis.
(Continued on next page)**

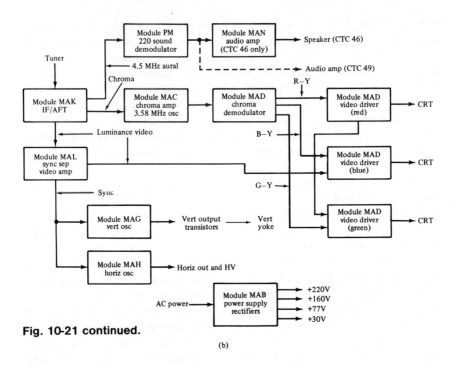

Fig. 10-21 continued.

(b)

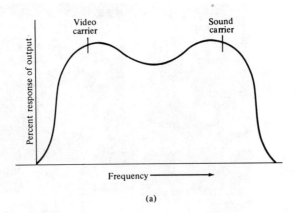

(a)

Fig. 10-22   **Coaxial cable arrangement for coupling the mixer stage to the IF section. (a) Normal RF frequency response curve; (b) intersection coupling circuitry.**

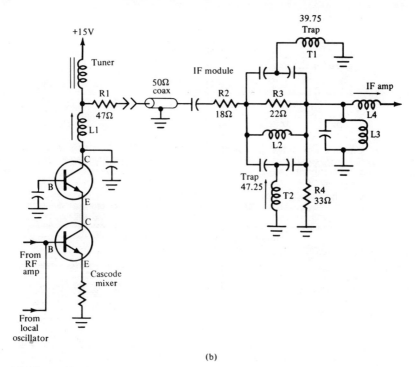

(b)

Fig 10-22 continued.

If picture symptoms indicate trouble in the "receiving" section, there may be a defect in either the tuner or in the IF amplifier. Accordingly, it is advisable to substitute a new IF module at the outset, to assist in localizing the malfunction. This test requires only half a minute, after the rear cover of the cabinet has been removed. In some receiver designs, the modular assembly swings out for inspection, and the rear cover is not removed. In the event that a substitute IF module is not available, another quick-check can be made as follows. With the IF module removed, a small capacitor is temporarily connected from the tuner output to the 4.5-MHz sound-input terminal. Since the 4.5-MHz intercarrier sound signal appears at the output of the VHF mixer stage, this test serves to indicate whether the tuner is operative. If there is no sound output from the speaker, the repairman concludes that the tuner is dead. This quick-check is illustrated in Figure 10-23. Its effectiveness is due to the fact that the IF amplifier normally contributes little gain for the sound signal.

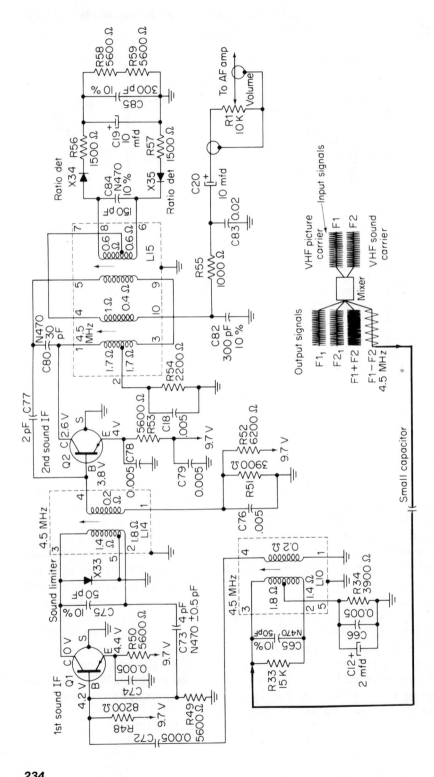

Fig. 10-23   Quick-check for suspected "dead" IF module.

Review Questions

1. Approximately how many maintenance adjustments are involved in color-TV set-up procedures?

2. What is the purpose of convergence procedure?

3. Name the two specialized test signals that are utilized in convergence procedure.

4. Describe the appearance of pincushion distortion.

5. Distinguish between static convergence and dynamic convergence.

6. How does an aperture-grille color picture tube differ from the older shadow-mask type of tube?

7. What are the two principal types of integrated-circuit packages?

8. Is the functional classification of a module always complete?

9. Explain a useful quick-check for a suspected "dead" IF module.

10. As a general rule, will an IF module from one brand of color-TV receiver operate properly in another brand of receiver?

Answers to Review Questions

Chapter 1

1. The first step to be observed in most electronic repair procedures is evaluation of trouble symptoms with preliminary diagnosis of equipment malfunction.

2. Two intermediate steps in electronic diagnosis procedures are first to observe the action of the operating and maintenance controls and second to make any appropriate quick-checks.

3. Rasping and scratchy sound reproduction throws suspicion upon the speaker because this trouble symptom is usually the result of a loose or warped voice coil that rubs against the pole pieces.

4. A typical color-TV receiver utilizes seven modules.

5. Signal tracing is a diagnostic technique in which an indicating instrument such as an oscilloscope is applied at successive points along a signal channel. Signal substitution is a diagnostic technique in which an appropriate signal voltage is injected at successive points along a signal channel.

6. A typical quick-check for a "dead" radio receiver indicates whether its local oscillator may be inoperative; local-oscillator voltage is coupled into an adjacent "good" receiver to determine whether heterodyne squeals are developed.

7. Single faults are most frequently encountered in malfunctioning electronic equipment.

8. Several of the basic tools used in radio, TV, and sound-system repair are screwdrivers, pliers, diagonal cutters, and a soldering iron.

9. The essentials of good soldering technique include correct positioning of the soldering iron so that the lead and the circuit-board foil are heated at the same time, use of sufficient but not an excessive amount of solder, and application of adequate but not an unnecessarily high temperature to the foil and lead.

10. Comparison tests are valuable in diagnostic procedures when the repairman lacks service data for a particular unit of electronic equipment.

Chapter 2

1. The indispensable test instrument for diagnosis of radio, TV, and sound-system malfunctions is some type of volt-ohm-milliammeter.

2. Many repairmen prefer DVM's over VOM's because of the higher indication accuracy that is provided by a DVM.

3. The basic generator used in a radio repair shop is an AM signal generator; in a stereo service shop, an audio oscillator (generator); in a TV repair shop, a VHF-IF sweep and marker generator.

4. The basic advantage that an oscilloscope provides over a TVM is its ability to display the variation of an AC voltage in time.

5. An in-circuit transistor tester differs from an out-of-circuit transistor tester in that the former provides a quick-check of transistor workability without disconnecting the device from its circuit.

6. A sound-level meter finds its principal field of application in analysis of acoustic environments.

7. The chief features of a video analyzer include facilities for signal-injection tests in all of the major sections of black-and-white and color-TV receivers, with a multiburst (bar-sweep) signal output for checking frequency responses of signal channels.

8. A picture-tube tester indicates the emission currents of electron guns in black-and-white or color picture tubes; a picture-tube test jig is a substitute picture-tube arrangement.

9. A frequency counter is a virtually essential instrument for a CB service shop because oscillator frequencies in CB transceivers are subject to very tight tolerances.

10. A high-voltage DC probe functions as an external multiplier for a VOM, TVM, or DVM.

Chapter 3

1. The central purpose of a mapping technique in electronic system diagnostic procedures is to provide a logical guide to electronic troubleshooting approaches.

2. A signal-path diagram is a generalized signal-flow diagram that indicates functional sections along the signal channels.

3. Pictorial diagrams are helpful in particular troubleshooting procedures because they indicate interconnections of units and/or equipment in a highly explicit manner.

4. An example of an elaborated block diagram is one that indicates operating frequencies of principal signal sections with normal signal-voltage levels.

5. A schematic diagram with specified signal/no-signal DC voltage distributions facilitates malfunction diagnosis because it provides significant supplementary data for preliminary malfunction analysis.

6. The purpose of a simplified schematic diagram is to show essential signal-processing features in a circuit section with omission of non-essential details.

7. It is helpful to have a block diagram with specified signal-voltage levels when troubleshooting a weak-output symptom.

8. If the base of a transistor is temporarily short-circuited to its emitter, the transistor normally becomes an effective open-circuit.

9. A skeleton circuit diagram usually provides no DC voltage data.

10. Series-parallel network reduction is accomplished by adding the values of resistors connected in series, by applying the product-and-sum formula to resistors connected in parallel, and by continuing the reductive procedure until the series-parallel network is represented as an equivalent resistance.

Chapter 4

1. The purpose of diagnostic tests in preliminary troubleshooting procedures is to identify the malfunction and to localize it insofar as possible.

2. Noise output from a "dead" radio receiver can provide localization clues because the noise level depends upon the number of operating stages between the fault site and the speaker.

3. The first test that should be made on a malfunctioning AM/FM receiver is to observe whether the AM section or the FM section is affected, or whether both sections are affected by the fault.

4. A "distorted output" trouble symptom is more involved than a "dead receiver" condition because the signal is not being stopped and because of the more involved tests that are required to analyze the distortion.

5. A practical analysis of the snow level on the screen of a TV receiver with a raster-but-no-picture trouble symptom consists of observing whether the level is low, medium, or high. The snow level depends upon the number of operating stages between the fault site and the picture tube.

6. Co-channel interference in a CB receiver can be reduced by use of a highly directional antenna and by using single-sideband transmission and reception.

7. "Audio rectification" interference occurs when a high-level RF signal overdrives an audio transistor and develops a rectified audio-frequency component.

8. The most probable cause of repetitive circuit-breaker tripping in a line-power unit of electronic equipment is a leaky filter capacitor in the power supply.

9. It is advisable to check for supplementary service data issued by a television receiver manufacturer when frequent callbacks occur and the receiver has been properly repaired.

10. A simple example of a phantom fault is replacement of a video-amplifier resistor, when the weak-picture trouble symptom is actually being caused by a deteriorated picture-detector diode.

Chapter 5

1. Several types of tests used in malfunction diagnosis of hi-fi stereo systems are signal tracing, signal substitution, frequency response, distortion measurements, separation measurements, and power output measurements.

2. An oscilloscope is a better signal-tracing indicator than a TVM because it shows if substantial distortion is present and what type of distortion is involved.

3. A lo-pwr ohmmeter has an advantage in resistance measurements when testing solid-state circuitry because it applies a very low test voltage that does not turn on the semiconductor junctions.

4. Voltage gain is not directly related to power gain; power gain depends upon the resistance values across which voltage values are measured.

5. Lissajous tests are made in preliminary analysis of audio-amplifier malfunction by feeding the input signal voltage of the amplifier to the

vertical channel of a scope, and feeding the output voltage from the amplifier to the horizontal channel of the scope.

6. Three common errors in component and device replacement are decimal-point errors in reading electrical values, reversing the emitter and collector terminals of a transistor, and connecting an electrolytic capacitor into a circuit with reversed polarity.

7. A harmonic-distortion test employs a single frequency, whereas an intermodulation-distortion test utilizes a two-tone signal.

8. An approximate output-voltage level for a tape deck is 1.5 mV.

9. A quick and efficient method of checking stereo separation is to connect the input and output terminals of the stereo receiver to a stereo analyzer; the number of dB separation is shown on meters.

10. A quick-check to pinpoint noisy devices or components in an audio amplifier is made by shunting a suspected unit with a capacitor and observing whether the noise output is eliminated.

Chapter 6

1. The basic distinction between a PA installation and a hi-fi system is that the primary function of the former is intelligible information transfer, whereas the primary function of the latter is distortionless sound reproduction.

2. A 70.7-V PA system is basically a constant-voltage arrangement; the audio line voltage is comparatively unaffected by the number of speakers that may be switched into or out of the line.

3. An example of a difficult acoustic environment is a large airport lobby with many corridors that develop lingering echoes, with a very high noise level when planes are arriving or departing.

4. Excessive delay time between direct sound wavefronts and reinforced sound wavefronts reduces articulation owing to syllabic overlap.

5. A typical speaker cluster comprises seven folded-horn type speakers mounted in a group facing the same direction on a wire-mesh support structure.

6. A magnetic-tape audio delay unit functions by recording an audio signal on the tape and then playing it back a fraction of a second later.

7. Positive feedback consists of in-phase feedback from output to input of an amplifier of audio system; in the case of acoustic feedback, effective control is provided by a directional microphone.

8. An audio mixer combines two or more audio signals and provides level controls whereby relative signal levels can be adjusted as required.

9. Balanced microphone lines are often used instead of single-ended lines to cancel hum voltage that may be picked up by the line.

10. A differential amplifier is basically a push-pull amplifier with a constant-current source in its common-emitter branch.

Chapter 7

1. Three basic types of radio equipment with which the electronic repairman is concerned are receivers, transmitters, and transceivers.

2. Signal tracing, sensitivity measurement, and alignment checks are three basic radio diagnostic test procedures.

3. Service-type AM signal generators do not ordinarily provide a pure sine-wave output.

4. A single-conversion superheterodyne employs one local oscillator and operates with one intermediate frequency; a dual-conversion superheterodyne utilizes two local oscillators and operates with two intermediate frequencies.

5. Off-frequency transmission in a CB transceiver is most likely to be caused by a defective transmitter quartz crystal.

6. A current-variation test of a "dead" AM broadcast receiver is made by connecting a milliammeter in series with the battery or power supply and tuning the receiver through its range. With the volume control advanced, an increase in current drain normally occurs when a station signal proceeds as far as the output stage. With the volume control turned to minimum, either an increase or a decrease in current drain will normally occur when a station signal proceeds as far as the detector.

7. The bandwidth of an AM broadcast receiver is 10 kHz; the bandwidth of an FM broadcast receiver is 200 kHz.

8. A sweep-alignment setup for an FM receiver employs a sweep-and-marker generator to energize the signal channel, and an oscilloscope to display the output waveform at the input or at the output of the FM detector.

9. The center frequency of a standard FM IF amplifier is 10.7 MHz.

10. Frequency markers are developed on a response curve by mixing a fixed frequency from a marker generator with the swept frequency from an FM generator.

Chapter 8

1. The three basic signals included in a TV broadcast transmission are a picture signal, a sound signal, and a control signal comprising synchronizing pulses.

2. The first practical scope checkpoint in a TF IF strip is at the output for the first-IF stage.

3. Subnormal signal-channel bandwidth results in loss of picture detail.

4. A demodulator probe develops the envelope of a high-frequency signal for display on the screen of an oscilloscope.

5. A low-capacitance probe facilitates waveform checks in high-imped-ance circuitry by reducing the load that is imposed upon the circuit by the oscilloscope input circuit.

6. The oscilloscope is connected across the emitter resistor of the mixer transistor in a front-end visual-alignment setup.

7. The approximate center frequency of a standard TV IF strip is 43.5 MHz.

8. A TV rcpairman checks for the presence of IF oscillation by measuring the DC voltage at the output of the picture detector; a substantial volt-age indicates that the IF system is oscillating.

9. An absorption marker appears as a "dip" or a "notch" in a response curve.

10. Sync buzz develops in a TV receiver when a transistor that processes both the picture signal and the sound signal is overloaded or incor-rectly biased so that it operates nonlinearly.

Chapter 9

1. Four principal signals that flow through the tuner and IF amplifier in a color-TV receiver are the black-and-white picture signal, the color sig-nal, the sound signal, and the control (synchronizing) signals.

2. The Y signal is separated from the complete color signal in the Y amplifier.

3. The chroma signal is separated from the complete color signal in the bandpass amplifier.

4. Color reproduction trouble symptoms may be caused by malfunctions in black-and-white receiver sections as well as malfunctions in chroma sections.

5. The two most important specialized color-TV test signals are a keyed-rainbow color-bar signal and a white-dot and/or crosshatch pattern signal.

6. The R-Y signal is the basic red-hue component; the B-Y signal is the basic blue-hue component; the G-Y signal is the basic green-hue component.

7. If a chroma demodulator has subnormal bandwidth, the baseline of a keyed-rainbow signal waveform will become curved.

8. Chroma-demodulator phases are checked with a keyed-rainbow gen-erator and an oscilloscope.

9. A vectorgram is displayed with an oscilloscope connected into the R-Y and the B-Y channels; the R-Y signal is ordinarily applied to the vertical-input terminals, and the B-Y signal is ordinarily applied to the horizontal-input terminals of the oscilloscope.

10. A dual-trace oscilloscope may be applied at the input and the output of a burst-gating section to display the gating pulse and the color burst simultaneously, with their relative timing.

Chapter 10

1. Approximately ten maintenance adjustments are involved in a typical color-TV set-up procedure.

2. The purpose of a convergence procedure is to focus the three electron beams to the same point on the screen of the color picture tube.

3. Convergence test procedures utilize white-dot and crosshatch signals.

4. Pincushion distortion appears as curved horizontal and vertical lines in a crosshatch pattern, with the amount of curvature increasing toward the edges of the screen.

5. Static convergence brings the three electron beams into focus at the center of the picture-tube screen; dynamic convergence brings the three electron beams into focus at the edges of the screen.

6. An aperture-grille color picture tube has red, green, and blue phosphors arranged as vertical stripes on the screen area, whereas a shadow-mask tube has the phosphors arranged as dots.

7. The two principal types of integrated-circuit packages are the round TO-5 housing and the rectangular flat-pack housing.

8. The functional classification of a module may be incomplete; its full function may be completed by another module or by chassis-mounted components and devices.

9. A useful quick-check for a suspected "dead" IF module is to connect a small coupling capacitor from the mixer output to the 4.5-MHz intercarrier-sound input to determine whether a sound signal may be reproduced by the speaker.

10. As a general rule, an IF module from one brand of color-TV receiver will not operate properly in another brand of receiver.

Appendix I

Resistor Color Codes

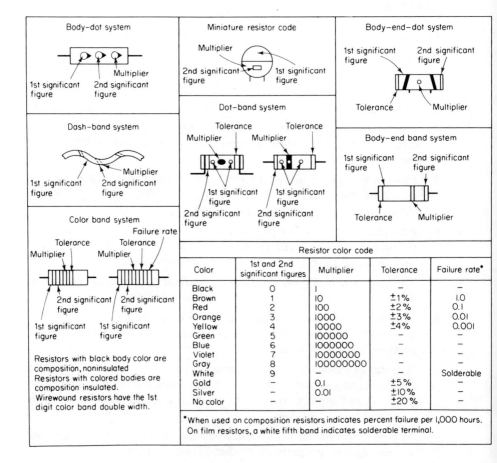

Resistors with black body color are composition, noninsulated.
Resistors with colored bodies are composition insulated.
Wirewound resistors have the 1st digit color band double width.

Color	1st and 2nd significant figures	Multiplier	Tolerance	Failure rate[*]
Black	0	1	–	–
Brown	1	10	±1%	1.0
Red	2	100	±2%	0.1
Orange	3	1000	±3%	0.01
Yellow	4	10000	±4%	0.001
Green	5	100000	–	–
Blue	6	1000000	–	–
Violet	7	10000000	–	–
Gray	8	100000000	–	–
White	9	–	–	Solderable
Gold	–	0.1	±5%	–
Silver	–	0.01	±10%	–
No color	–	–	±20%	–

[*]When used on composition resistors indicates percent failure per 1,000 hours. On film resistors, a white fifth band indicates solderable terminal.

Capacitor Color Codes

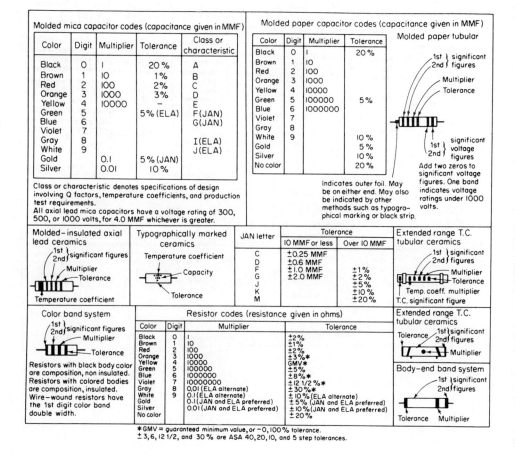

Molded mica capacitor codes (capacitance given in MMF)

Color	Digit	Multiplier	Tolerance	Class or characteristic
Black	0	I	20 %	A
Brown	1	10	1%	B
Red	2	100	2%	C
Orange	3	1000	3%	D
Yellow	4	10000	–	E
Green	5		5% (ELA)	F(JAN)
Blue	6			G(JAN)
Violet	7			
Gray	8			I(ELA)
White	9			J(ELA)
Gold		0.1	5% (JAN)	
Silver		0.01	10 %	

Class or characteristic denotes specifications of design involving Q factors, temperature coefficients, and production test requirements.
All axial lead mica capacitors have a voltage rating of 300, 500, or 1000 volts, for 4.0 MMF whichever is greater.

Molded paper capacitor codes (capacitance given in MMF)

Color	Digit	Multiplier	Tolerance
Black	0	I	20 %
Brown	1	10	
Red	2	100	
Orange	3	1000	
Yellow	4	10000	
Green	5	100000	5%
Blue	6	1000000	
Violet	7		
Gray	8		
White	9		10 %
Gold			5 %
Silver			10 %
No color			20 %

Indicates outer foil. May be on either end. May also be indicated by other methods such as typographical marking or black strip.

Molded paper tubular

1st / 2nd significant figures
Multiplier
Tolerance

1st / 2nd significant voltage figures

Add two zeros to significant voltage figures. One band indicates voltage ratings under 1000 volts.

Molded-insulated axial lead ceramics

1st / 2nd significant figures
Multiplier
Tolerance
Temperature coefficient

Typographically marked ceramics

Temperature coefficient
Capacity
Tolerance

JAN letter	Tolerance	
	10 MMF or less	Over 10 MMF
C	±0.25 MMF	
D	±0.6 MMF	
F	±1.0 MMF	±1%
G	±2.0 MMF	±2%
J		±5%
K		±10 %
M		±20%

Extended range T.C. tubular ceramics

1st / 2nd significant figures
Multiplier
Tolerance
Temp. coeff. multiplier
T.C. significant figure

Color band system

1st / 2nd significant figures
Multiplier
Tolerance

Resistors with black body color are composition, non insulated. Resistors with colored bodies are composition, insulated. Wire-wound resistors have the 1st digit color band double width.

Resistor codes (resistance given in ohms)

Color	Digit	Multiplier	Tolerance
Black	0	I	±2%
Brown	1	10	±1%
Red	2	100	±2%
Orange	3	1000	±3%*
Yellow	4	10000	GMV*
Green	5	100000	±5%
Blue	6	1000000	±8%*
Violet	7	10000000	±12 1/2 %*
Gray	8	0.01 (ELA alternate)	±30%*
White	9	0.1 (ELA alternate)	±10 %(ELA alternate)
Gold		0.1 (JAN and ELA preferred)	±5% (JAN and ELA preferred)
Silver		0.01 (JAN and ELA preferred)	±10 %(JAN and ELA preferred)
No color			±20 %

*GMV = guaranteed minimum value, or −0,100 % tolerance.
±3, 6, 12 1/2, and 30 % are ASA 40,20,10, and 5 step tolerances.

Extended range T.C. tubular ceramics

1st / 2nd significant figures
Tolerance
Multiplier

Body-end band system

1st / 2nd significant figures
Tolerance   Multiplier

Disc ceramics (5-dot system)	Ceramic capacitor codes (capacity given in MMF)							High capacitance tubular ceramics insu-lated or non-insulated

Disc ceramics (5-dot system)				Tolerance		Temperature coefficient PPM / °C	Extended range		High capacitance tubular ceramics insu-lated or non-insulated
							Temp.	Coeff.	
	Color	Digit	Multiplier	10 MMF or less	Over 10 MMF		Signifi-cant figure	Multiplier	
	Black	0	1	±2.0 MMF	±20%	0(NP0)	0.9	−1	
	Brown	1	10	±0.1 MMF	±1%	−33(N033)		−10	
	Red	2	100		±2%	−75(N075)	1.0	−100	
	Orange	3	1000		±2.5%	−150(N150)	1.5	−1000	
	Yellow	4	10000			−220(N220)	2.2	−10000	
	Green	5		±0.5 MMF	±5%	−330(N330)	3.3	+1	
	Blue	6				−470(N470)	4.7	+10	
	Violet	7				−750(N750)	7.5	+100	
	Gray	8	0.01	±0.25 MMF		−30(P030)		+1000	
	White	9	0.1	±1.0 MMF	±10%	General		+10000	
	Silver					purpose bypass and coupling			
	Gold					+100 (P100) (Jan)			

Disc ceramics (3-dot system)

1st } significant
2nd } figures

Multiplier

High capacitance tubular ceramics insu-lated or non-insulated

1st } significant
2nd } figures

Multiplier
Tolerance

Voltage (optional)

Temperature compensating tubular ceramics

1st } significant
2nd } figures

Multiplier
Tolerance

Temperature coefficient

Ceramic capacitor voltage ratings are standard 500 volts, for some manufacturers, 1000 volts for other manufacturers, unless otherwise specified.

Current standard JAN and ELA code	Button silver mica	Molded flat paper capacitors (commercial code)	Molded flat paper capacitors (JAN code)

White (ELA)   Black (JAN)

1st } significant
2nd } figures

Multiplier
Tolerance
Class or characteristics

Button silver mica

1st (when applicable) } sig. fig.
2nd for 1st
3rd for 2nd

Multiplier
Tolerance
Class

Molded flat paper capacitors (commercial code)

1st } significant
2nd } figures

Voltage
Multiplier
Black or brown body

Molded flat paper capacitors (JAN code)

Silver

1st } significant
2nd } figures

Multiplier
Tolerance
Characteristic

Molded ceramics	Button ceramics	Stand-off ceramics	Feed-thru ceramics

Molded ceramics
Using standard resistor color-code

1st } significant
2nd } figure
Multiplier

White band
Distinguishes capacitor from resistor

Button ceramics

1st } significant
2nd } figures

Multiplier

Viewed from soldered surface

Stand-off ceramics

1st } significant
2nd } figures

Multiplier

Tolerance
Temperature coefficient

Feed-thru ceramics

1st } significant
2nd } figures

Multiplier
Tolerance
Temperature coefficient

Transistor Identification

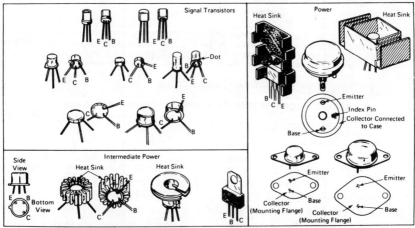

To Test a Transistor You Need to Know Three Things

1. The Basing Configuration (E, B, C, or S, G, D). The Diagram Above Shows Some of the More Common Configurations. If the Transistor Type Number Is Available, the Basing Configuration Can Be Found in the Manufacturer's Handbook. Also, a Schematic May Provide This Information.
2. The Type (NPN or PNP). This Information Can Come From the Circuit, Schematic, or Manufacturer's Handbook.
3. The Power Class. See Diagram Above. (Signal, Intermediate Power, or Power.)

Appendix IV
Diode Polarity Identification

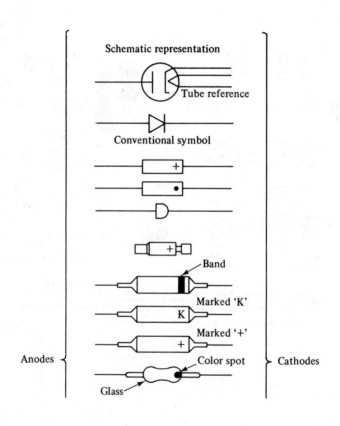

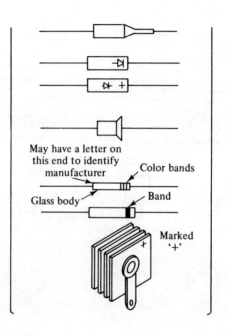

Basing Identifications for Typical Transistors

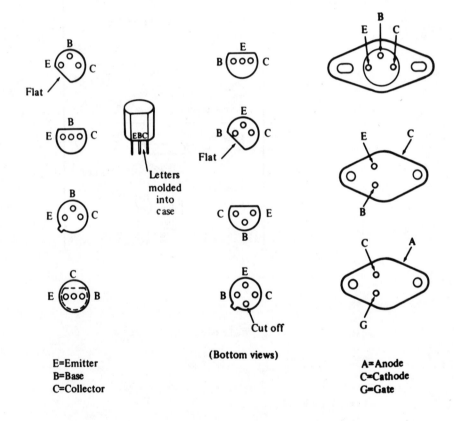

(Bottom views)

E=Emitter
B=Base
C=Collector

A=Anode
C=Cathode
G=Gate

Index